GOLD FEVER

by Helen E. Wilson

DEDICATED to my husband Roy (Bud), who was an encyclopedia of knowledge. His Navy career took him three times around the world and he had duty in many foreign ports including service on a gunboat up the Yangtze River in China. After he retired from the Navy, Roy's love of the out-of-doors, jeeping, hunting and fishing still broadened his scope and in the years we spent in Jarbidge District, he learned as much, if not more, about the district and the forest land around as the "old timers."

Published by Helen E. Wilson
4830 Harbinson Avenue
La Mesa, California 92041
First Printing, July, 1974
Second Printing, August, 1977
Third Printing, May, 1987

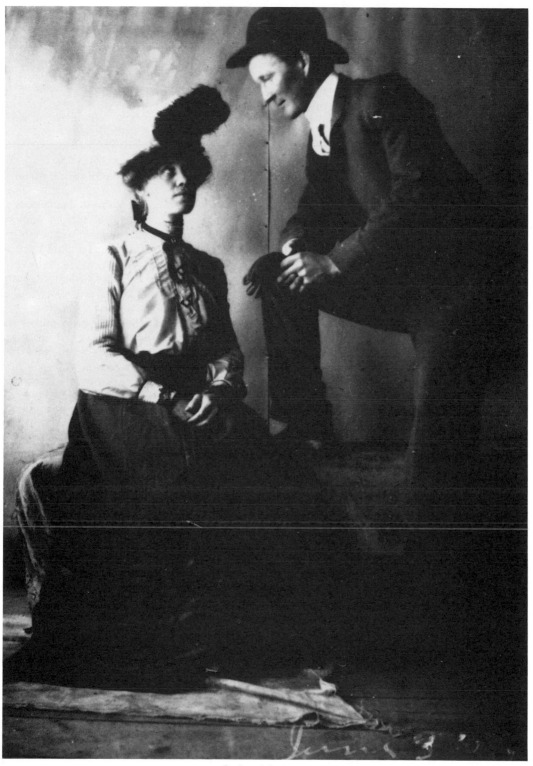

Jack and Hattie

ACKNOWLEDGEMENTS

Countless books tell about the gold rush days. Reminiscent authors have written Western Americana histories. It is difficult to sift fact from hearsay, but in this Nevadan story I have endeavored to tell facts. Sources of information which I used were many: United States Government Field Reports of 1911 and of 1923, by Frank C. Schrader, writings and minutes of the Jarbidge Commercial Club, Mining and Engineering Journal, Chicago, Illinois of 1912. Humbolt National Forest and 71 Livestock Assn. fifty year celebration commemorative pamphlet of 1967, The Times News, Twin Falls, Idaho, where I was given access to the early issues of that newspaper.

I am grateful to the late Nick Vucovitch, who, many years ago, spurred me on to write the story, and to numerous other people who wanted to know the history of the beautiful Jarbidge Canyon.

After my dear Mother passed on in 1958, I took her many pictures, souvenirs and mementoes to look through. Upon delving deep into an antique carrying satchel, I found a precious stack of letters, actually tied together with a blue ribbon. They were letters from my father to my mother dating back to when she was Hattie Marshall (1904), also letters at the time and after Jack's arrival into Jarbidge, February 7, 1910.

Devouring those yellowed pages of love, promises and news — each as fragile as the spiderwebs of New Hope — I found myself reliving those dangerous, exciting but romantic days of my father and mother's life. Their meeting, marriage, hardships in 'boomtowns' and babies being born.

During the two weeks it took me to read and absorb those letters, I barely came out of the cocoon I had put myself into, to live my own life as wife of Roy G. Wilson; but learned and wrote with complete confidence that Jarbidge had shone as one of the brightest stars in Nevada's history.

I wish to acknowledge my love and indebtedness to my late husband, Roy (known as 'Bud' by the Jarbidgeites). Without his endless support, belief and constructive criticism it would not have been possible for me to develop and complete the Jarbidge stories. His tireless hours, helping me with research and traveling over the States of Nevada and Idaho to meet with people who told me their stories and experiences as they freighted into the camp.

My sincere thanks for pictures go to Barbara Herlan, Nevada Historical Society, to Bess Cordell, my Aunt Pearl Martin, Vivian and Don Billick and Mother, whose hobby must have been picture taking, and she did her own developing. Also thanks to my sister Grace, Roland Hawes, Jewel Martin, Alice Fletcher Hicks, George Urdahl and Elsie Clark Whiteside for permission to print from tapes they made especially for the book. The stories they remembered were highlighted with tragedy and humor that I would otherwise have missed.

However, stories of Jarbidge, The Devil Canyon, were written largely from my own recollections. Some names are fictitious but the people were real and the events took place.

Many thanks go to Mrs. Fred Goodridge, La Mesa, for the hours she spent editing my manuscript for punctuation, grammar and phraseology. Also to Mrs. Esther Skelton, Elko County Recorder, where I spent day after day either reading and taping or typing on Esther's typewriter excerpts from the most orderly kept file of newspapers: The Elko Daily Free Press and Elko Independent. The Elko Daily Free Press deserves a special bow for its feature story of the stage driver murder and stage robbery.

I should like to express appreciation for the interest and teachings I derived from my instructor Ronal Kayser (Author Dale Clark) who is teaching at the University of California, San Diego, Extension Course.

Helen E. Goodwin Wilson

La Mesa, California
April, 1974

PREFACE

In the Northeastern corner of Nevada just nine miles from the Idaho border, where the mountains balance on Idaho's ranch and agricultural flatland, is a storied community that has lived lustily — almost died and now lives again. It was founded and flowed to prosperity on the tide of prospecting and mining and ebbed to nearly obscurity when the rich gold and silver metals petered out and the companies turned to richer fields.

Today, Jarbidge, with a winter population of twelve to fifteen and a summer population of one hundred-odd, is finding new stirrings in the field of fishing and hunting and just getting away from the city life.

Jarbidgeites will tell you it could never be a large town because of the limitations of its own geography. Cradled in a narrow canyon and surrounded by a national forest it is compelled to limit its population to the homes that can be built within the acreage of the townsite.

However, there are a few that live in Jarbidge and others come back to visit who are descendants of the old rollicking mining days. Citizens of the freeways and the cities' hot cement jungles have added to the summer and fall population. Fishermen and hunters love the cool, smog-free air and like to hear their voices echoing against a background of mountain greenery. It is a far cry from the old days, and yet, the dirt street, false front buildings, log houses and ramshackle mills are kept as a remembrance.

The beauty of the Humbolt National Forest, surrounding the townsite, is bringing scores of visitors to the area. People come who like to paint the scenery on canvas, snap the phenomenon with a camera, or writers who want to tell the lifestyle of one of the last frontier towns with no telephones in a story article.

A passerby does not "see" the same house that the family who knew that dwelling as home "see" when they look at the same building. The wild west cowtown was one kind of village to the eyes of the Eastern schoolmarm, and a very different place as seen by the cowboys who drove the herds up the trail. And so with the scenes and incidents depicted in this book. Here Jarbidge and Pavlak are described and the experiences of their inhabitants are narrated from the viewing point of persons who were then present and participating in the gold rush and subsequent mining eras.

THE LEGEND – JARBIDGE

The Westerner left his names naturally and casually upon the land. Some were names borrowed from the Indian, or creeks, the mountains and natural formations. Some names were drawn from the pioneers' experiences, unusual or disastrous.

Many tales have been told about the ancient legend of how Jarbidge got its name.

The Shoshones of the Duck Valley Indian Reservation are among the best authorities. One aged Shoshone Indian revealed the legend that his grandfather told him years ago.

"Ja-Ha-Bich" was a huge giant with teeth so big that they could be seen far away. In describing this monster's ears, the Indian picked up a dishpan at hand and said, "Ears big like this pan, eyes big my hand," and he doubled up his fist.

According to the Indian speaker, the giant became enraged at the sight of fire and whenever the Indians built fires in the Jarbidge Canyon he roared to make the air shake, and to throw stones as big as a man's head for a distance of a half-mile. The monster was a cannibal who lived by eating human flesh.

The one Indian who escaped the clutches of this giant, so the aged Indian said, went into the canyon to strip the bark of saplings to fashion bow strings. He lighted a fire and "Ja-Ha-Bich" saw him and was wild with rage. The giant walked out on the rim of the crater, which was his legendary home, and consumed with anger, he started toward the thoroughly terrified Indian. The Red Man put out his fire and, running for his life, escaped from the canyon and the giant.

Another legend of the Devil Canyon, which is the meaning of the word "Ja-Ha-Bich," goes back far into the Indian history, centuries before the day of the white man.

Ancient Indian tribes met and fought great battles in the canyon and surrounding mountains. Braves, women and children were killed and many of the survivors suffered. Winters were cold, and blood stained the snow and earth. The tribes feared this bloodshed was wrong. Then the mountains erupted and out flowed volcanic ash and rock – and so the Craters were made. The Indians saw this fire, smoke and heat rise into the heavens as the mountains trembled. They knew they had angered their GREAT SPIRIT OF THE UNIVERSE and they prayed to be saved as they fled from the Devil Canyon.

The eruption of fire, lava and smoke ended and the Legend of the Devil Canyon was named. The name of Ja-Ha-Bich was more easily pronounced Jarbidge by the White Man.*

*Indian artifacts – points, scrapers, blades and bones have been taken from caves, beside creeks or rivers, or elsewhere in the Jarbidge District in proof that the Indians lived there. Displays are in Museums, Historical Societies and private collections. The Nevada State Museum offers Anthropological Papers – Number 11 of the Deer Creek Cave excavation. Desert Research Institute, University of Nevada, Reno, offers Technical Report – Archeological Survey in Eastern Nevada, 1966, No. 2: by Don D. Fowler.

CHAPTER 1

To the eyes of the eagle winging overhead, the Jarbidge region in the State of Nevada, was one of lofty, rugged, snowclad peaks, sharply slashed canyons and gulches through which tumbled and raced headlong streams.

Stands of aspens' near-white trunks and leafless branches stood in knock-kneed fashion on the hillsides. They reflected the winter's frigid grip.

The eagle circled in the sky and glided with air currents. With wings quietly outstretched, he rested on invisible hills of air or updrafts, on which he could glide and soar for hours over his territory looking for food below.

As he flew over snow-covered summits and huge snowdrifts, he saw a roaring avalanche set off by something — or maybe by nothing. He then soared eastward to a lake which shone like a brilliant emerald set in towering pine and fir trees of the Jarbidge Wilderness. The February sky held dark snow-clouds and sharp noisy winds lashed over the steep-walled chasms which slipped nearly a mile below the Matterhorn, Cougar Peak, denuded Black Dome and the "Craters."

Winging his way to the forest, he saw the fantastic gallery of massive stone statuary along the canyon walls which suggested a primeval sculptor's carvings. These weird, reddish, tan and ash-green spirals stood guard over the canyon's entrance and appeared in shape half-human, half-animal.

To the eagle hovering over the area looking for squirrel and rabbit, the statues seemed to change shape hour by hour as the sun moved across the sky, they also changed year by year as the winter winds, rain and erosion smoothed or carved their surfaces.

The powerful and graceful bird flew over the caves in which Indians had lived over two thousand years before, but had left naming this the "Devil Canyon." So diversified was the region's topography that only a single hour of his flying was needed to make the transition from the sagebrush zone to the scrub cedar and cottonwood, then on to the pine and fir.

The eagle's keen vision could not see the veins of gold ore in the mountain ledges nor the free gold in the streams' gravel beds. But as he winged northward he saw the groups of migrant people, some afoot, others on horseback; lines of pack mules loaded with prospecting and assayers' supplies and the bare necessities to survive in the new Jarbidge Mining Camp, located in the Humbolt National Forest. Now and then a light wagon pulled by two sweating horses traveled over the muddy pair of ruts that left the flatland of Idaho and curled, climbed and plunged through the snow into the once isolated canyon.

The "King of the Air" viewed two horses floudering and falling down a gulch into the canyon. As he circled for a close-up view of the horses lying there in the snow, he focused on a man making his way down the mountainside to the animals.

Jack Goodwin worked his way down the steep, snowy mountainside carrying his rifle. During the hazardous descent he grasped protruding rocks, limbs and sagebrush extending above the snow covered ground, only to slip and slide many feet into a snowbank. He got up, wiped the snow from the gun barrel, brushed off his face and clothes, shivered and continued down the mountain in a zig-zag manner. All the while Jack wondered if he would have to destroy either one or both of the horses which had just rolled several hundred feet to the bottom of the canyon.

. . . Jarbidge Canyon viewed from Crippen Grade.

He had tried to help them regain their footing by holding and pulling their reins and lead rope, but they fought so desperately on the sliding rocks and snow that he knew his life was in danger if he held on any longer. When he reached the bottom one horse was up and seemed all right, but the other one was down, lying flat on his side. How badly is he hurt, thought Jack. Dead? — Dazed ....? "Good God!" Blood was running from a jagged cut on the animal's jaw and another over the eye. "I believe he has lost that eye. Could he be injured inside his head — or body?"

After he bent down and ran his hand over the black's battered head and inspected the bleeding places, he found the cuts were not very deep so he filled his large handkerchief with snow and by holding it against the bruises, stopped the bleeding. He then examined the horses' legs and couldn't find any broken bones.

Jack got to his feet. He felt sick, his head reeled. What should he do — what else could he do? So he stepped back and raised the rifle to shoot the animal. No! He just couldn't . . . couldn't. The animal was still breathing, he could see that —

Soon the black raised his head. He had recovered from the daze; slowly and with painful groans he struggled to his feet. "That's a good horse." Jack could hardly speak because of the lump in his throat, but he stroked the animal's head and neck and talked to him, then walked him a few steps. Although the battered critter favored one leg, it wasn't broken. How fortunate, thought Jack.

Camp was only about one-half mile away. So he led the horses to the Pavlak camp. Tom Beadle, his partner, was there waiting for him.

"Whatever happened, Jack? I've been worried about you."

3

"Those poor horses fell, slid and rolled for several hundred feet over rocks, snow and timber. My God! I tell you Tom, that was the worst thing I ever saw in my life," said Jack as he told Beadle about his two-day prospecting trip in the rugged craters east of the Jarbidge Canyon.

"You know I've seen rough country with you in Wyoming and Colorado, but there are mountains in this district go up from the river for thousands of feet and some seem almost straight up.

"I tried to come down Snow Slide Gulch when the horses lost their footing on the sliding rocks." Jack looked as though he was reliving that horrible experience as he continued. "The bay came out without a scratch but the black, as you can see, doesn't look as though he fared so well. Sure was glad I didn't destroy the animal, do believe he'll get well. I will clean the wounds and put some salve on them, may even blanket him awhile; then see if he will eat some oats."

"I'm sorry as can be," said Beadle. "I guess you wonder sometimes, Jack, why I asked you to come to this Godforsaken Jarbidge country, but we will make it. Trust me! It just takes time."

This steep-walled cut in the earth, the Jarbidge Canyon, runs for fifteen miles before it joins the Idaho line. Along the canyon floor flows the fast moving Jarbidge River and its merging tributaries, swiftly cutting its way north from the mountain springs to the Bruneau River connecting with the Snake and Columbia Rivers eventually to reach the ocean.

John D. Goodwin, better known as Jack, was a prospector. Somehow he managed to learn mining practices and grew to understand the language of the earth and rocks. This sudden call to a new place awakened the excitement and urge to join the gold strike.

John Dennis Goodwin "Jack" or "J.D."

Looking into the Jack Creek (or First) Crater which rimmed Jarbidge on the East.

Jack, a young, strikingly handsome blond man, thin and agile, had great vitality and endurance. People noticed the freshness, the clean new look about this young westerner. Also his clear, steel-blue eyes and often tensely held thin lips changed with his moods. Although he was overly popular with the opposite sex and had captivating manners, he still was a man's man; talkative, merry, imaginative and filled with dreams of success, wealth and importance. Jack was dependable and his many friends knew that. Yet, when men pried into his business he would most obviously stop talking.

The knowledge of ore formations and outcroppings came quickly for Jack and he could tell by the colors what precious metal would be found — or, to quote him — "If it was ore-bearing or *just country rock.*"

Prospectors were led on by the phenomenal richness of the Goldfield and Tonopah strikes and they hoped each new one would be a bonanza for them. Some hit it rich but many didn't. Jack joined the great rush to Goldfield when he received a stake from a Wyoming man, but the expected fortune did not materialize so now he was eager to leave for the new gold camp of Jarbidge, in Elko County, when he received his friend Beadle's letter. He needed this reassurance, but most of all he needed money to keep his wife and baby.

Tom Beadle, a well known assayer from Cripple Creek, Colorado, also Wyoming and Nevada, had arrived in Jarbidge soon after its discovery. His first thought, after he was set up for business and saw the opportunities, was to send for Jack. So he wrote on December 15, 1909: "I arrived here with my assaying equipment and am doing a rushing business. This district promises to be a real boom and looks rich as any I have ever seen.

"The fact that you played the game through under such handicaps as you did in Goldfield and Happy Creek, had quite a bearing on the Chicago people and they are anxious to take a chance if you are. They have money and lots of it and simply ask that we devote our best judgment and time to the development of some property or a good mine. Could you come over this way and we can stake some claims together? Very soon we can send for Mrs. Goodwin and Baby Grace."

What a coincidence. Hattie was pregnant again and wanted to go to Kansas City to visit her sisters and have their child there. Even though they would be separated again, "It will only be for a few months, Hattie dear," Jack assured her and himself. "I'm a good prospector and miner and it takes big money to develop a mine and those Chicago people have it, don't you worry." Jack put his arm around Hattie. "I love you and Gracie very much, Honey, and will do anything for you and must not lose you two. The baby isn't due for nearly five months and you can visit your sisters and have some city life. I have enough money to send you and Gracie on the train and you can rent a house of your own instead of staying with your sister Lizzie this time. I'll send you more money soon."

Jack folded the letter from Beadle and tucked it away in its envelope and after shaking the ashes down in the grate he added two more pieces of wood. Hattie knew what it meant to be loved by Jack, she was a mature woman now and she loved him, surely she could appreciate this western man's innermost desire to find that golden rainbow just over the horizon.

5

It took very little time for Hattie to pack and be ready when the train left Goldfield two days later. She was excited and had forgotten the hardships — almost. A fleeting regret and anxiety about how Jack would get along came over her as they rode in the buggy to the railroad station. After they boarded the train she saw him waving from the platform and Gracie threw kisses to him with her tiny hand. Tears came to Hattie's eyes, but Jack started away in a hurry as though he had to attend to other business.

CHAPTER 2

It was five years ago that Jack traveled the hard and stony route of a professional game hunter. Earning his living by hunting elk and deer, supplying meat for the people of the mining camps of Wyoming and Colorado. He had left his home in Park City, Utah, when he was seventeen. Restlessness stirred in his blood and he wanted to be free, to explore the great unknown West.

Jack was an excellent shot and took pride in his accomplishments with his reliable 30-30 Winchester rifle.

It was also five years ago that Jack met Hattie Marshall in Encampment, Wyoming. She had come there to visit a married sister and enjoy a badly needed holiday from her strenuous work in Kansas City. She had planned and dreamed of this month of adventure among the majesty of the mountains and crystal clear running water.

U.S. mail stage

Central Telephone Operators, Encampment, Wyo.

7

Her life had been one of work and deprivation as she was the fifth born of seven children. When her mother died of pneumonia and her father succumbed four years later, it left three quite young children. Fortunately the older ones were old enough to take care of the younger.

The romance in the serenity of the forest, the charm in the stately mountains and trees and the music of the gurgling brooks provided the surroundings in which Jack and Hattie fell in love.

He taught her to snowshoe and ski, hunt and shoot. She was stimulated by the friendliness and warmth of the people in the small town.

Hattie was entertaining; she played the guitar and sang such enchanting old tunes as "The Bird in the Gilded Cage" and "After the Ball is Over." Her hazel eyes were large and round and she had a lovely full-lipped rosy mouth. Her soft brown, wavy hair brushed out to waist length and she dressed it in the most attractive, fashionable coiffure of the day. She was unlike any of the girls Jack had known and he yearned for her with a tender passion.

To Hattie, Jack was dazzling, a figure of romance from a world of excitement and adventure. He was a new breed of man in comparison with those she knew in Kansas City. There, Harold Love had been her steady boy friend. He gave her such lovely gifts as a "La Reine Paris" opera glass and a black Scottish Skye terrier dog. Hattie cherished this smart terrier and named him Frisky. He had long black hair and some hair covered his eyes. Frisky's long and low body and short legs led Hattie to refer to him as "two dogs long and half a dog high." He was a well behaved dog so she took him with her where ever she could.

8

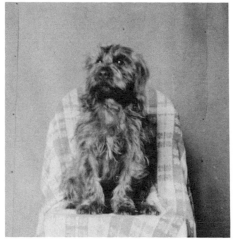

Hattie thought of Harold and how considerate he was, also, how conservative. She knew he loved her but wanted to wait until he had substantial savings before he married. Had he lost her to a more exciting man? Jack represented a world she did not know, but with him, she dared to venture into.

The time was near for her to return to work and the city. She had learned to do many things the West offered, but not how to fish. She found a pole, line and extra snell hook, just ready to be used, in the wood shed. After she had put on a large floppy hat over her hair, she walked down to a mountain creek. The soil was damp and spongy because an early snow fall had just melted. Hattie hoped she could cast without tangling her line behind her.

She didn't know one fly from another, but the one on the leader was bright enough. At first she snagged everything in sight — willows, dead logs in the stream and even her own hat — but seemed to retrieve the fly each time. Finally she cast the hook near a large rock overhanging the stream and immediately a trout struck. She was so surprised she almost dropped her pole. She let her line go slack. The trout leaped, shed the hook, and was gone.

Hattie stared unbelievingly at the fly now floating on the water. She cast again and again in that pool but got not even a nibble. So she moved upstream. Before she could cast, a grasshopper landed in the water. He'd no sooner lit than a commotion ensued. Hattie saw the bodies of two fishes rising as they fought for the grasshopper. Then the water lay calm again, the fish — and the grasshopper — gone.

The grasshopper bait was a good idea, thought Hattie. She spied one on a nearby rock.

Ugh! that sticky, ugly thing! She grabbed for him, the hopper leaped to safety beyond her reach. She followed him, grabbed again — again missed. The grasshopper sat on a piece of driftwood, daring her to catch him.

This time Hattie leaned over and surprised him. In a flash she took the big hat from her head, hit the driftwood and when she looked to see if she had gotten her bait, there he was under the hat, mashed and not moving anymore. Now she would take the fly hook off and place the snell hook on the leader. How could she touch

9

that insect. Its eyes were looking at her. As she picked him up those long, spiny legs stuck her fingers. After some time the feat was accomplished; she had the snell hook on the leader and had threaded the hopper onto the naked hook. Might as well get used to it, she thought.

Hattie dropped the grasshopper into the water and everything happened at once. She remembered to set the hook this time and began reeling and pulling in a large rainbow trout. When she had it on the bank, she knelt beside the flopping beauty and stared at it in wild delight. They are rightly called rainbow, having such beautiful colors and stripes. She stroked him as he finally lay limp — sorry she had taken him from his cool home.

The grasshopper had slipped up the line. He only needed to be pulled down again onto the hook and reused. But she had to get the hook out of the fish's mouth. It was then that Hattie discovered that trout must have small teeth.

"Ouch!"

"Let me help you, Sweetheart."

Hattie got to her feet when she heard Jack's voice. She was bursting with pride as she showed off her catch. Jack came closer and she thrilled when he took her hand. For a long moment their eyes met, then suddenly, she was in his arms, his lips soft and damp against hers. Her heart was a wild bird beating against its cage. She was excitingly happy. She felt his muscles tremble and the fast beat of his heart. They kissed for a long time.

"I know that I have very little to offer you," Jack whispered rather timidly. "I know that life with me will be very different than the life you are used to, but I want you for my very own. Hattie, will you promise to marry me before you leave for Kansas City?"

This proposal had caught Hattie still uncertain. Did they have enough in common to be compatible? She saw how her sister, Charlotte, lived with a miner. She wondered if she really knew what it was to spend years living around in mining camps and bringing up her children in such an environment.

"Jack, darling —" tears filled her eyes — "I love you very much. Please give me a couple of weeks at home, in Kansas City? I will return to you. Just a little while." Hattie realized a frustration she had not anticipated.

His arms released her slightly, he felt a brief disappointment, but quickly drew her close again and pressed his lips against her warm full lips. She responded even more ardently than he had expected. Her hand stroked his cheek and wandered around his neck. It necessitated a little struggle for him to force his lips away from hers.

"Hattie, darling!" His voice was low and husky. He had suddenly thought of a way to hold this pretty brown-haired girl he loved so much.

"Please leave Frisky with me. I will take as good care of him as though he was my very own dog. Then I know you will come back to me. Besides I have become very fond of that smart terrier."

Hattie left Frisky with Jack and returned home. His proposal stayed fresh and beautiful in her mind, and she thought carefully. For two months he waited for her to come back. In his letters he wrote, "I will never give up hope that you will be all mine someday, and very soon. I received your loving letter this morning, would rather have found you here than a letter. We can't always have our way, but will live in hopes. Frisky went hunting with me today and I killed three deer. When we were hunting we came across a big bear track but we thought it best not follow him."

On the second of December, 1904, Jack wrote Hattie that he had a financial supporter who had asked him to take a contract in Goldfield, Nevada, the new booming gold camp. He could make a *strike* there and as soon as he got settled she must come and marry him.

Jack was afraid he would lose Hattie, so when he left Encampment he hurried by rail to Kansas City and there they were married. After a brief honeymoon, Jack went to Goldfield, hoping that he could send for his bride very soon.

CHAPTER 3

"Don't be afraid. Take a shot at anybody that bothers you." Thus wrote Jack from Goldfield to Hattie in February, 1905. "I have a place for you now and will send money by Wells Fargo. This is the letter that I've wanted to write for two long months. It is a long hard trip for you to make alone, this end from Tonopah to Goldfield being much the worse.

"Come by train to Denver, Ogden and Reno. Then there will be a long slow train ride on the narrow gauge from Reno to Tonopah. Will be looking for you so come to me in a hurry. Your anxious husband, Jack."

Hattie arrived in Tonopah without mishap, but a very tired person. She found that Jack had made a room reservation for her at the Mizpah Hotel. Although it was midnight when she arrived, the town was busy and noisy. Tonopah was five years old and growing fast. The hotel, a newly built brick building, had a small lobby done in red Victorian paper. There were stoves and kerosene lamps. On the second story, reached by stairs with a banistered rail, her room, partitioned half way to the ceiling, was furnished with an iron bedstead and clean, made-up bed. On the cheap pine cabinet sat a white china bowl and pitcher and a chamber pot was beneath the cabinet. Hattie was glad Jack had made arrangements for her room because the desk clerk told her there were few rooms left. She would wash and get to bed as she had to be up early.

It was seven A.M. when the stage pulled in front of the hotel.

"Stage for Goldfield leaving in five minutes!" the driver shouted as he opened the lobby door.

The passengers hurried outside to board the coach. Hattie turned as she heard her name called.

"Mrs. Goodwin, Jack asked me to watch for you and see that you arrive safely in Goldfield. He'll meet us there."

"Oh! Thank you, Mr.—."

"The name is Adams, just call me Zeke."

"My husband wrote me this would be the worst and roughest part of the trip." Her smile was a mixture of half-shy, half-fearful.

12

"Let me help you aboard, I've taken care of your baggage."

Zeke Adams was a lean, raw-boned man with a bristly beard. He was reputed to be the best reinsman in this part of the country. The driver was king. He was an important man and he knew it.

Hattie thanked the driver and as she entered the coach the musty, sweaty smell of leather and the lingering dust of the roadway was still apparent.

The coach could accommodate six passengers if they were jammed in. What a relief, after she was seated next to a young woman, that only two men passengers came aboard. She was glad they wouldn't be crowded.

The woman was flashily dressed, no doubt a dance hall employee. Her brassy-colored hair was elaborately coiffured, heightened with a spray of paradise feathers and a velvet bow. She was a large woman but so tightly corseted that her breasts were pushed up high, nearly escaping from the lace that edged the front of her dress. The vivid magenta of the costume accented her florid complexion. It was impossible to judge her age because of her heavy makeup, but she was probably nearer forty than the twenty she must have hoped she appeared.

"My name is Belle," said the woman sitting beside Hattie. "I just heard Zeke call you Mrs. Goodwin. Is this your first trip to Goldfield?"

"Yes, it is, Belle, and I don't mind telling you I'm apprehensive."

"Well, don't you worry. I've been over this damned, rough road many times and Tab here and I will see that you meet your husband before we leave you in the Gold Camp."

Tab sat across the coach from them. He was a handsome, slender Italian neatly dressed with an expertly trimmed mustache. He wore a white broad-brimmed hat and a Prince Albert coat of broadcloth. Hattie thought he might be a gambler — or? She would not ask their business, maybe not the best idea.

The hostler brought out a hot rock wrapped in burlap to put at each passenger's feet and a robe to cover the ladies' legs. "May be a cold trip as February is usually cold and wet in this country," he said.

13

There was no payroll in the boot this trip so there would be no need for an express guard, or shotgun messenger. Zeke climbed up to his seat, grumbling about getting out on time.

The coach lurched forward. A frisky near-wheeler cut a few didoes as they started.

"He's got to make up that minute he lost," said the fourth passenger. This little man with the cast in his right eye and wearing a bright red vest, sitting next to Tab, was a drummer.

"What time will we get to Goldfield?" he asked.

"We'll get there in time for a late supper tonight," Tab said. "We have two stops to change teams in this twenty-five-mile run."

The drummer rambled on about how he wanted to stretch his legs at those stops. "I know it takes little time to get a tired team off and a new team on as harness and horses go together." He continued, "You know I've heard that drivers are sure cranks about their horses, also about their whips. They brag that they can pick a horsefly off a leader without the horse feeling a thing. There is a beeswaxed, silk popper at the end of the lash that snaps like a firecracker."

He talked on about his liquor salesmanship, about the scenery and the black clouds which threatened a coming storm. Finally he subsided, but only for a short time.

"You have some queer names for your towns," he said, breaking the brief silence. "Take Tonopah, it means 'hidden spring water.' My first time out here, but the water is hidden all right, didn't see any springs. But that is good for my business. Eh?"

Rand, the drummer, turned to Belle. "Why are you going to Goldfield? Looked to me like Tonopah was a pretty lively town."

"Tonopah is all right," Belle said in a surprisingly soft voice, with none of the harsh qualities so many girls in her profession developed from talking above the noise in the smoke-filled saloons. "I work where the money is and the Goldfield boom is red hot. They will have electricity and water connections to the homes this year and that town will be a modern city." She smiled at Hattie. "I hope your ribs and elbows aren't sore from the pitching from side to side and the frightful rocking

14

you will get on the coach ride. Zeke is a good driver, but he never loses a minute unless there is a good reason like a hold-up or a flash flood or somethin'. But I shouldn't say such things and get you to frettin'."

"Never worry about me, I am doing fine." Hattie tried to conceal her mounting anxiety. "I heard a man at the hotel say the stage was robbed two days ago."

"They had a payroll aboard," said Tab. "But the robbers were taken prisoners. There was a sheriff riding the Concord. However, passengers don't get hurt in holdups," Tab explained. "Road agents seldom rob women, they may even be polite to them." Nevertheless, Hattie's imagination had built up this journey into a perilous adventure.

The stage clattered across small bridges and along the rutty road. Soon it swung onto a long, steep grade that bordered an arroyo. The teams slowed to a laborious walk. Willows and rocks practically brushed the coach on one side. When they reached a fairly flat bench in the road, Zeke pulled the horses to a halt.

"We are only three miles from a relay station," shouted Zeke. "But if I don't rest these horses they would die before we got there."

The relay station was at the fork of the road. One branch ran on to the left to Klondike, the other road went to Goldfield.

As Zeke pulled the stage up in front of the station the hostler came out and Zeke said, "Rub the horses down and blanket them for a while — they are hot." He jumped down and opened the door of the coach. "You folks rest here and refresh yourselves in the station. Sorry we are driving into a rainstorm, but do not worry about that. Been through lots of 'em."

Hattie was hoping her stiffness of body would not show as she stepped out of the coach. She would be glad when this trip was over and she was with Jack again.

It seemed only a few minutes until Zeke was calling, "All aboard!"

They boarded the coach and Hattie slipped into the corner to rest. Soon she was asleep as she was exhausted. The rough spots of the road awakened her now and then, yet she relaxed for most of an hour.

It was nearly nine that night when the stage topped the hill from which they could look down on the lights of Goldfield. Out of the dance halls and saloons the tinkling of the honkey-tonk pianos and husky-voiced singers rang into the night. The two main streets were crowded with ore wagons, freight outfits and mule trains loaded with supplies for outlying camps. The boardwalks were jammed with men going in and out of gaming places and saloons. In front of each establishment kerosene flares advertised its entertainment.

A night shift of carpenters was working on the skeletons of a new mercantile store, a bank and a hotel, and the sound of saws and hammers blended with the shouts of drunken miners.

The scene appalled Hattie. "What are so many men doing out on the streets?" she asked.

"The miners are all here blowing in their wages," Belle told her. "There is no night in this town, especially since this is Saturday."

"When do they sleep?" Hattie said, puzzled.

"Tomorrow is Sunday. They can sleep all day, if they can find beds. Hundreds of bunks are rented three shifts every twenty-four hours," Belle explained. "One man tumbles in when the preceding one rolls out."

The stage made a path through the traffic and drew up at its station. There stood Jack waiting for its arrival. But there was a fight going on between some drunken men around him. Angry shouts filled the air.

The driver, Zeke, set the brake and came down from his seat. He ripped out a furious oath. "Godalmighty, let my passengers out and get away from this coach. Settle your fight somewhere else."

As Zeke opened the stage door he helped Belle down onto the ground. Hattie followed but a panicky fear came into her throat. In the placid world she had left, men like these did not exist.

As Jack caught her arm and was holding her to him, her teeth were chattering and her small body was shaking.

"Don't worry about that little fight," Jack told her cheerfully. "You are here with me and that is all that matters now, my dear."

Hattie introduced Belle and Tab to her husband and when they saw that she was well taken care of they slipped away into the crowd.

She clung to Jack's arm as they moved down the sidewalk crowded with drifting men. "Don't be afraid, Sweetheart, I have reserved a room for us at the leading hotel in town. What you need is sleep, you're dead tired after this long day."

The reserved room was on the third floor. It was clean and quite extravagantly furnished for a new mining camp, and the double bed comfortable.

Once during the small hours Hattie was awakened by the sounds on the street. Group singing and the music from the honky-tonks she heard. She went to the window and looked out. The first faint streaks of day were sifting into the sky. The steady thump-thump of feet on the sidewalk as the men shifted to and fro was almost as dense as when the stage had arrived.

Hattie crept back into the warm bed and dropped back into sleep and when she wakened it was with the sun sending its warm rays into her eyes.

When the Goodwins entered the dining room the proprietor waved to them to sit at a cozy table at the window. Did he sense they were newlyweds? After breakfast Jack took Hattie to the little house he had rented for them.

"We may not be here for long, Sweetheart, this place will do for a while."

She was happy and made the best of anything as long as they were together.

Later she followed Jack, occasionally on prospecting trips. By May of 1906, a child was to be born and Hattie went back to her sister's house in Kansas City to have their child. Grace Harriet was a lovely blond baby.

A girl! and Jack had kept talking about a boy, but he wrote: "My own dear Hattie and Baby, Just got your wire and glad you are all right. Take good care of that baby, she won't do to prospect, but she can do the cooking and get the wood and water and that will help some."

"Now, Hattie, take good care of yourself and Baby. Don't worry about me. Have the doctor and nurse until you are strong, as I never in this world can replace you.

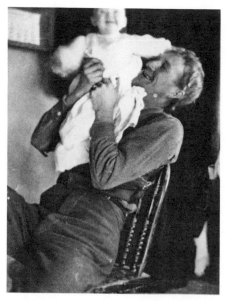

You name the baby, I don't know how to name a girl. From your loving and happy Papa. J.D. Goodwin."

He wrote from Eureka, Deephole, White Mountain, Beowawe, Hawthorne, Humbolt House, Buena Vista, Lovelock and Winnemucca, Nevada. Also from Denio, Oregon. That he was lonesome, tired, and working too hard and wanted to make a *lucky strike* so that he could stay with his family — this would be the last trip he would take when his wife and little one came back to him.

Jack's letters came often, they were loving and Hattie grasped at the sincerity he tried to convey. But, she knew he was still looking for that *bonanza*.

When Hattie and Gracie came home to Goldfield, Jack was there and they were a happy family. Jack was proud of his wife and baby and never missed a chance to show them to his friends. Their stay was short in Goldfield, then on to Hart and soon to Happy Creek, California. Hattie never complained, but followed Jack wherever he went.

Grace was a friendly and lovable child in disposition, much like her father. She thought everyone should speak to her as he or she passed the house — or was it a tenthouse in Hart? This was a desert country and because of the scarcity, water had to be bought by the barrel. It came very expensive and must be conserved. Hattie kept her family clean and even Gracie was given enough water to bathe her doll now and then.

17

CHAPTER 4

Jack boarded the northbound train for the northern corner of the State of Nevada. He had put Hattie and Gracie on the eastbound train three days ago and had some finishing up to do before he left Goldfield; some mining equipment to sell, a team of horses and a claim. He was glad he had encouraged Hattie to stop off at his mother's and sisters' in Salt Lake City.

He knew she had been unhappy about moving again, and, she was right, he must settle down and build a home for his family. Maybe Jarbidge would be just the perfect place. His intentions were the very best, but — somehow prospecting got in his sights and blurred those good resolutions. His early life had taught him to be daring, willing to endure hardships, even sufferings and frequently real dangers. Now he had a family to care for.

The wind was blowing and snow falling when he arrived in Elko. Zero weather chilled him. Southern Nevada didn't get quite that cold. Maybe he could afford a warm Mackinaw with a sheepskin collar — yes, he would need one.

Jack was a fastidious man, always clean shaven and his fine light-blond hair neatly cut. Generally he wore gloves, even for his work and he chose to wear puttees over the legs of his breeches.

On inquiring about the road to Jarbidge, Jack learned there was none from Elko across the summits and that he would have to go by train to Hollister, Idaho. A long way around, but the only route into the isolated country.

From Hollister it took Jack three days to get to Jarbidge, approximately seventy miles. He went part of the way by freight wagon then continued for the last twelve miles by horseback on a trail through deep mud, slush and snow. Some of the going was flat plateauland, and as he rode over the flat-topped mesa surrounded by tortuous, rimrocked cliffs, his thoughts kept returning to Wyoming where he had met his hazel-eyed, lovable, city-bred girl. But as he neared the canyon rim the trail became steep and rugged. He pulled his felt hat down and turned the sheepskin collar up to shield his neck and face from the wind and snow that felt like tiny wires hitting the bared skin. His horse did not want to proceed against the driving wind and snow, and had to be prodded along. Many men were walking, some were riding mules, just any way to get there.

18

When Jack arrived on February 3, 1910, Beadle was in camp to welcome him to the Jarbidge Gold Strike. He found the scene a lively prospectors' utopia. A rag town — with five hundred tents extending for three miles along the banks of the flood-swelled Jarbidge River. Snow covered the ground but much of the country had been staked on snowshoes without prospecting the hidden claims. In some instances trees were used as stakes. Considering the mode of travel and route into the canyon, Jack was amazed that each day fifteen to twenty newcomers entered the district.

Nevada State Historical Society Photo

The altitude of the camp was 6200 feet and the Jarbidge Mountain Range on the east of the canyon attained a height of nearly 11,000 feet. On the west the canyon walls rose to two summits of 8400 feet and 8488 feet before they descended to the ranch country of Charleston. Stimulated by the show of gold in the hillsides and streambed, the immigrants took the hardships of isolation, frigid sub-zero temperature and snow storms with winds blowing drifts of fifteen to twenty feet.

Nearly six hundred men populated the Jarbidge camp, and not a woman. Prospectors, promoters, freighters and businessmen swarmed to the new bonanza and the usual tent saloon flourished selling their beer warm and liquor straight.

Nevada State Historical Society Photo

Beadle was glad to have Jack there.

"How was your wife and baby when you left Goldfield, Jack?" asked Beadle.

"They were fine, Tom. Thanks for asking. I must build a house for my family, can't move around the country like I have been doing, you know. Did you hear we are expecting our second child and Hattie went on to Kansas City to be near her sisters and a doctor? I assured her we wouldn't be separated long and I would build a house for us, then send for them as soon as she and the little one could travel."

Beadle congratulated him and agreed that Hattie would have better care in the city.

"I'm anxious to let her know I arrived here safely and also to hear from her," Jack continued.

Beadle directed him to the temporary post office tent.

Upon inquiring, Jack found there were over four hundred names on the post office list and mail was going out once a week. Since there was no official post office in town, a reliable man distributed the mail. And, since there was no cancellation rubber stamp for the outgoing mail, the name Jarbidge, Nevada, and the date was written across the two-cent stamp.*

At first, George Walters carried the mail in once each week on his pack train from Three Creek, Idaho. He received $50 per month, but business was growing so fast that arrangements for delivery twice a week — and soon three times a week — had to be organized. Walter Smith brought mail from Gold Creek by horseback, however he was paid by donations.

From Elko, the county seat of the Jarbidge district, mail was sent in without recompense by the Elko Commercial Club. This sometimes amounted to several packhorse loads a trip.

It was about three days before Jack found a tent and bed of his own. There was no doubt he appreciated being taken in and sharing a tent with Beadle and George Winkler, but the men crowded in to talk every evening. He had no privacy nor time to write to Hattie.

Jack found plenty of work and knew this was going to be a real Boom Town. Wildcat claims were selling fast. A man told him he would buy any claim that he could locate, so Jack went out prospecting often and got some good claims.

Prices for food and commodities were exorbitant. Flour was twelve dollars a hundred pounds, potatoes fifteen dollars for a hundred pounds, oats twelve dollars a sack and hay ten dollars a bale. Tod Hunter bought a pound of butter and as he entered the tent, he said, "Jack, I had to pay one dollar for this butter — guess we'll have to spread it mighty thin."

"I'd say so, Tod," and Jack shook his head in amazement. "Guess I'll have to quit smoking my pipe, because I paid one dollar for a pound of tobacco today. Glad I

According to research: United States Postal Service, Roy M. Nail was appointed postmaster of Jarbidge, March 5, 1910. Winthrop W. Fisk appointed July, 1912. John B. Scott Fleming appointed May, 1913 and kept the appointment for nine years.

Hattie Goodwin received letters with handwritten date and Jarbidge, Nevada, across the stamp — May 15, 1910, May 17, 1910, May 27, 1910, and as late as June 5, 1910; also some stamps were not cancelled at all. These the author has.

didn't bring my team of horses, it would have cost one hundred and fifty dollars a month to feed them."

Tod squatted on his heels and fashioned a smoke. As he laid his tongue along the paper, he said, "Jack, did you see the two big tent saloons open today? Of course neither one has a permit, but the forestry service has been real lenient in the camp."

"Yes, I saw them and they must expect a big gambling business as there's a table in each saloon. Sure, you know that a professional gambler can pick a town of prospectors clean in a few good poker games," Jack warned. "I'll go in for a drink, but I'm not a gambler; then too, I have other places for my money."

The gasoline street lamps which had been installed by most of the business houses lit the street brilliantly that night and Jarbidge looked like one of the "old time Eldorados."

Nevada State Historical Society Photo

Charles S. (Syd) Tremewan was the first Supervisor of the Humbolt National Forest and Jarbidge lay within the forest boundaries. Mr. Tremewan's term of office ran from 1908 until 1913. He recalled that many sheep, cattle and horses grazed the Humbolt Division when that land was put under national forest management and he became supervisor. Joseph Asdala, the first forest ranger in the Jarbidge District, got his appointment the year of 1913.

When the Jarbidge gold rush started, Syd Tremewan found himself confronted by the building of saloons and the illegal sale of liquor on United States Government land. Barrels of whiskey and kegs of beer were freighted into the town on muleback. The forest service had decided to secure indictments against the saloons at the next meeting of the federal grand jury and in the meantime were not interfering.

A townsite was laid out in Jarbidge and a mining monument was established on the ridge just west of the town, between the river and Bear Creek. People obtained special use permits or lot rights from the forest service officer for ten dollars. These lots were to be used by those who intended to build a cabin or legal business.

The Tent Town following the discovery of Gold.

Nevertheless, some who had paid ten dollars for a lot right, and many who had just pitched a tent on a certain piece of town property, were illegally selling to newcomers who did not know about the National Forest Property Law. Some men paid as much as one hundred to three hundred dollars then resold choice lots for eight hundred dollars, giving the buyer only a bill of sale.

Claim jumpers, promoters and out-and-out crooks floated around the camp which kept men keyed to a high pitch. Men did not always act rationally with reports of penniless prospectors becoming wealthy mine owners overnight. Those who paid hundreds of dollars for choice lots in the camp kept an eye on their property. The saloons were crowded until late hours and barrels of liquor were consumed.

There had been no unusual trouble until Bobby Byrne pitched his tepee tent on Jim Miller's lot. They had an argument and Miller went to his own tent about two hundred feet away. Later, in exchange of gunfire, Miller shot and killed Byrne.

A court was assembled at Jimmy Cameron's tent, "The Jarbidge Hotel," which one hundred men attended. Mr. E. Klein, a New York attorney, presided as a prosecutor. The assembly chose twenty-five men as jurors and twelve men were examined and sworn in. The trial was set for that afternoon and after a thorough investigation of the case and the examination of fifteen witnesses, Miller was exonerated. It was then that Mr. Klein had a discussion of plans for a permanent peace officer. Billy Ross, an old-time miner of immense stature, was elected to fill that office and deputies chosen to patrol different districts. The assembly then elected a coroner. The people established a board of arbitration for the settling of location disputes, making Jarbidge a more law-abiding and organized camp.

After hearing about the shooting, Elko County sent in a judge and deputy sheriff to see if they could lend a hand, however when they arrived the town was peaceful.

The old prospectors, who had the habit of gophering from place to place, had left camp. The genuine mining men who had come to the district were just waiting for the first opportunity to make a careful inspection of the properties being held by prior locators, who had ninety days to do their work on the claims they held. Many allowed the locations to elapse and the waiting miners and prospectors took up the holdings.

A meeting was held at the tent of Hudson and Wilson where forty men were present. Bourne and Wait were appointed to decide the best route for a road out of the camp. They would survey and estimate the cost of a route to Twin Falls and ask for the assistance of the Twin Falls Commercial Club.

In order to be closer to their located ground, Jack and his partners, Beadle and Winkler, were moving by pack horse up the creek to the new community of Pavlak, two miles south of Jarbidge. Jack was making some canvas sacks in which to carry their supplies and equipment. He had a contract to dig a tunnel, a shaft and some location holes. He would set the wage as he felt a "good man" was hard to find; also he knew he would have to wallow in the snow. But he was eager and energetic, and had such a good reason to make money.

CHAPTER 5

Jack Goodwin was curious, and an avid listener to stories the old-timers told. Soon he had pieced together in broad outline a history of the Jarbidge country:

Sometime in the 1890's during the time when Mormon Pathfinders were striking out in all directions in search of new areas to settle, two of these men came exploring and prospecting into the Jarbidge Canyon. Jack never learned their names — partly because the newcomers did find gold and were shrewd enough to keep their discovery to themselves. They built a primitive mill, an arrastra, to pulverize the ore and rocks which they found. But the two Mormons left one day and never returned.

Jack wondered about the lost sheepherder's mine which he had heard about in the early history. Could that have been Vishim, a sheepherder, who later found the arrastra covered with debris and carried out a piece of high-grade quartz? But there was no stampede to the area then, probably because sheepmen and cattlemen had no interest in minerals; and so the arrastra's hiding place was never revealed.

Other men were curious about Jarbidge's beginning, too — F.C. Schrader went there as a United States Geologist to do some field work and make a report; A.L. Rinearson, a surveyor, made maps of the area; Tom Beadle read the report and saw the maps. So when he and Jack were running some assay samples one day, Beadle told Jack what he had learned.

"David Bourne, his wife, and partner Ben Collins prospected the Jarbidge River in September of last year and as he went upriver to the Gulch which is now called Bourne, they found gold in the pannings." Beadle continued and Jack listened intently. "They discovered the gold was washing down from the hillsides of the gulch so Bourne located that ground.

"Then John Escalon came into the canyon from the opposite direction, from Charleston, over the summits between here and the Charleston Ranches. He found a ledge of high-grade ore within ten feet of the surface and named his claims Pick and Shovel. On the heels of these discoverers came Mike Pavlak and Peter Thuro, who located some claims two miles up the canyon from the Bourne property. So that is why we call this settlement Pavlak," said Beadle.

Looking at a canyon tent town, how would a newcomer become aware of his destiny? thought Jack. He listened with great interest to the history of this district.

24

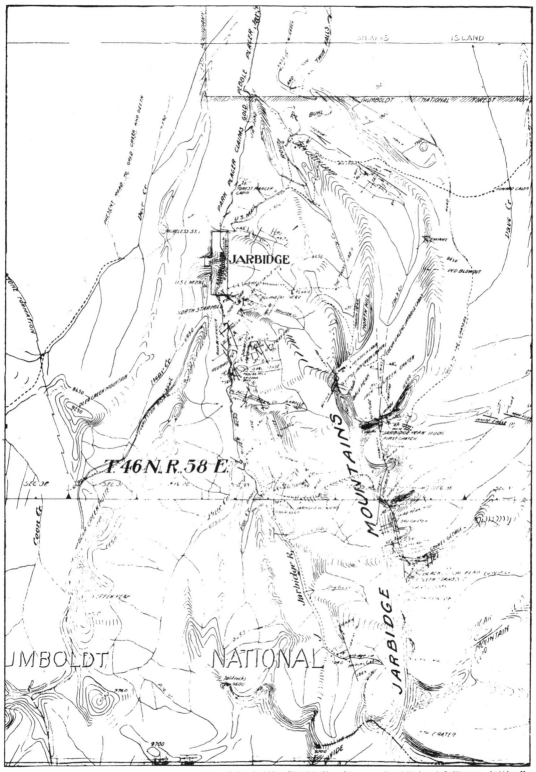

Map of the Jarbidge District, Nevada. Copyrighted by A. L. Rinearson, Jarbidge, Nev.

The booms of the mining West had been the Aladdin's Lamp and eyes of the world were turned beyond the Rockies. His ears were tuned to such names as Bourne, Escalon, Pavlak and others. Jack wondered if some day those names would be history.

Up and down the Bruneau Valley, even in the San Francisco press, news spread like fire that Bourne had discovered GOLD and uncovered a fortune in Nevada. Prospectors dropped their pans, investors and capitalists grabbed their hats and closed the doors of their offices to join the greenhorns fresh from the East and the newcomers of all sorts.

But it wasn't easy getting to the isolated Jarbidge Canyon in the Humbolt National Forest of Northeastern Nevada. There were only two ways to arrive there: Walk or ride horseback. Nevertheless, men went, bogged down in mud as they crossed the flatland from Hollister, Idaho, then plunged through the deep snowdrifts as they climbed the steep, winding trail leading into Jarbidge.

Within a month fifty men had arrived and the Jarbidge Mining District was organized at a meeting at which a recorder and deputy recorder were elected.

"Soon after I got into camp," Beadle told Jack, "with sixteen men present, we raised a purse of fifty dollars to bring in the first mail. The ramshackle camp of tents and lean-tos was being built in the canyon, at the widest flat beside the Jarbidge River, just north of the Bourne Gulch."

Pavlak found gold and sold after a few months. Brunn and Kinney, who were acting for themselves and for Pittsburgh and New York parties paid one hundred and twenty-five thousand dollars for the Pavlak group of claims and their managing superintendent came to Jarbidge fully equipped.

"What do you think, Tom, of that assay of three hundred dollars to the ton that we ran on the Pavlak ore the other day?" asked Jack.

"A good sample," said Tom, "the man told me he got it from the bottom of a forty-foot shaft, also that the ledge was thirty feet in width and showed free gold from wall to wall."

Clark & Fletcher Mill

Pavlak Mill

The Jarbidge-Pavlak Mining Company constructed a mill which furnished employment to scores of men. Timber for the mine and mill were cut and hewn in the district. For the day in which it was built, this mill was first class and up-to-the-minute in every respect, as was its process for treating the ore. It consisted of many rooms and a tower building measuring 40x106 and extended 109 feet into the air. It started operation August 15, 1911, and ran intermittently for four months, but then, owing to the financial difficulties and the low extraction of good grade ore, it closed in February of the year of 1912. The total output had been $10,000.

Tom Beadle knew he would not fail to find the richest ore of the district. Since he had taken geology when attending college, he knew considerably more about mining than the majority of the discoverers. He and two of his friends, Winkler and Benane, fought their way through the snowdrifts up the mountainside and lay claim to what Beadle considered the best ore in the district.

It was a blustery, snowy day, January 11, 1910, when they set their location post in the snow, supported it with some loose rocks, and nailed a tobacco can to the post in which was a prescribed form for each claim and the name "Bluster" taken from the weather of that day.

Bluster Mill under Construction

The rich ore of the Bluster later proved to be one of the mines which gave Jarbidge fame as the richest gold producing camp in the State of Nevada.

The Bluster Consolidated Mines Company was formed and Beadle elected president and Jack, treasurer.

Tom Beadle taught Jack Goodwin the trade of assaying and he learned fast and well. Men brought samples of ore into the office to determine the yield of gold and silver; the main metals of the district. Jack wrote Hattie how hard he was working, and he was glad to learn the trade; Beadle and he accomplished a lot, they were good friends.

Because Tom was out of the camp frequently and left Jack to run the office, he became one of the best assayers in the district. He would have as many as

27

twenty-four samples per day and often run out of gasoline for the retort furnace. He worked from six in the morning until after dark everyday because samples were coming in too fast for one man.

When Beadle returned he praised Jack for his good work and told him that he got an option on the ground Jack had located. He had to pay three hundred dollars for the option and was going back for the adjoining ground.

Before Beadle would go out again he told Jack they must attend the town meeting to separate the camp from the Humbolt National Forest. At the meeting a committee of five residents drafted resolutions to be sent to United States Senators Nixon and Newlands of Nevada, also to the Bureau of Mines, Washington, D.C. It was very important that the townsite be taken out of the national forest so that business houses and cabins could legally be built and the small area be under the jurisdiction of Elko County. They hoped there would be no resistance from the Federal Government.

Form 832
(Revised November, 1908)

UNITED STATES DEPARTMENT OF AGRICULTURE

FOREST SERVICE

SPECIAL USE PERMIT

Prosp. Cabin, *'0/10/10*, *Humboldt* National Forest.

Permission is hereby granted to *J. D. Goodwin*

of *Jarbidge* *Nevada*, to use the following-

described lands: *About ¼ acre, situated on the*
(Describe the lands to be occupied, if unsurveyed, by metes and bounds with reference to a road or stream or well-known landmark:

west side of Jarbidge Canyon about one
right of way by terminal points, direction, and ands occupied)

mile below the mouth of Pine Creek

Approx Sec 28, Township 46 N., Range 58 E.,

M D M & B.

for the purpose of *developing his mining claims*
(Briefly but clearly describe the use, giving area of inclosures, length and width of right of way, etc.)

U. S. DEPARTMENT OF AGRICULTURE
FOREST SERVICE

News spread that the mining district was a 'real boom' and that the Bourne Mine had $27 million worth of gold and silver ore in sight. Both the New York and the Chicago Engineering and Mining Journals were interested and wrote asking for maps showing the situation of the unmapped new mining district. All this publicity made the population of Jarbidge swell to fifteen hundred.

There were those who came to the camp to build a town, not looking for riches which could be gained from the prospector's pan or the miner's pick and shovel. Among them were men who wanted to build and own a hotel, restaurant, general merchandise store, a saloon or such enterprise for an early developed camp.

Two stores, three assay offices, three restaurants, two tent hotels and many saloons were open for business. A doctor had arrived in camp. Also a blacksmith had opened a shop. Wives and families seldom came until the excitement had subsided, as it was a man's world. But when the district showed promise, families started arriving and permanent buildings were erected and a semblance of social and sanitary order maintained. Harlots and opportunists wasted no time in arriving when the atmosphere was conducive to a successful business.

Slim Walsh and Vane Whiteside, among other freighters, had established pack trains between Three Creek, Idaho, and Jarbidge. By daylight the pack trains made up of eighteen or twenty mules and horses were being loaded with food, blasting powder, caps, fuse, hand tools and the basic necessities for a boom camp. Slim and Vane were highly skilled packers and would not let anyone else load their animals. They worked fast, packing the loads evenly; and to hold the pack securely while traveling over the rough and steep trail into Jarbidge, the packers threw a complicated diamond hitch in the rope to keep the load from shifting. Once the animals were all packed, the freighter mounted his lead horse and led the first pack mule which had a bell around its neck; the rest of the string followed.

The hardships which Slim, Vane and the freighters experienced along the trail woke them up out of their sleep in a sweat. But they were brave young men and returned to the camp many times with more food and supplies.

They came across the rimrock and down into Wilkins' Hot Springs Ranch, better known as "Kitty's Hot Hole." The pack trains forded the East Fork of the Jarbidge River and pulled up the steep terrain to the Wilkins' Island where Kitty and her brother ran their horses for a summer range. The large Wilkins' Island and the small Dave Island were so-named islands because they were high tableland plateaus surrounded by deep rimrocked canyons in which the East Fork River, the Dave Creek and the Jarbidge River flowed.

Bourne Canyon

29

CHAPTER 6

On March 12, 1910, the case of Laura Kitty Wilkins vs. C.C. Logan was being tried in the district court. It was an ejectment suit brought from Owyhee County where it was first filed in the probate court, but on account of the high waters and bad roads the case was stipulated to the district court in Caldwell, Idaho. Had it not been for the discovery of Jarbidge Gold Camp, the case would never have been brought to court.

Jack Goodwin was interested in this lawsuit. He had wondered why that place on the route into Jarbidge was called Kitty's Hot Hole. Freighter Slim Walsh told him there was a hot spring which bubbled out of the ground and ran into East Fork River. Kitty Wilkins claimed ownership of that piece of land.

Kitty, the only daughter of the Wilkins family, was a beautiful, spirited woman with glowing blue eyes and dark brown hair. Besides being an excellent horsewoman, she became an accomplished pianist when she attended the Sacred Heart Academy in Ogden, Utah. She had many friends, partly because of her charity and love for the sick and less fortunate.

When the Wilkins' Hotel burned in Tuscarora, Nevada, in 1879, the family moved to Bruneau Valley and started a ranch. From their small band of horses they soon owned hundreds of head, roaming across the Bruneau Desert.

Kitty took her brother, John, as a partner in the horse business and at the turn of the century they ran as many as sixteen thousand to twenty thousand head.

Kitty belonged to an important segment of the American frontier; she was one of the pioneers who took leadership roles in taming and developing the West. They were a breed of hardy risk-takers, who had the courage and foresight to become the region's first merchants, ranchers, bankers and employers. And the Western woman's role was not merely to "stand behind" the successful man. Often the wife, widow or daughter became the acknowledged head of the business operation. (Western States had woman's suffrage before the rest of the country — Wyoming, fifty-one years ahead of national woman's suffrage.)

Kitty Wilkins' registered brand was the "Diamond" and she was toasted the "Queen of Diamonds" in San Francisco, Chicago and Kansas City, where her trips took her to the horse markets. She had contracts to furnish Eastern and Western

30

markets with carloads of "saddle-broke" horses at certain intervals of the year. The United States Government brought remount stallions to breed with some of the better Wilkins' mustangs. Therefore the United States Cavalry, one of the ranch's regular and best customers, was supplied with many good mounts.

The Hot Hole was not really a ranch, but served as Kitty's headquarters for her summer grazing island. Every April, after she had her horses rounded up from the Bruneau Desert and driven into the Hot Hole, the horses were kept there until summer and time to drive them up to the good grazing of the Wilkins' Island. From the top of the rimrock to the sheer drop-off into East Fork River, the men built a rock fence to keep the horses from going back into Idaho; but as soon as they were on the grazing island they never left, until they were driven out in the fall.

Logan "located" as a squatter at the Hot Hole after the discovery of gold at Jarbidge. He maintained it was the terminal of the road and all freight and passengers must be unloaded and distributed at that point from freight wagons to light wagons, pack mules and saddle horses. He also said that travel was increasing and the new gold camp needed that terminal. Kitty claimed a possessory right to the piece of land in the canyon and that under the present conditions it was producing her five hundred dollars a month. Logan, the defendant, denied Kitty's possession and said that as she had never held the land in good faith he had built a tent boarding house at the hot spring.

The significance of this lawsuit was a clash of two economic stages, two life-styles, in the West. Logan, running a "tent boarding house" for the patronage of freighters and travelers en route to the new gold camp – Kitty representing an earlier, ranch "spread" economy and life-style. Similar clashes have occurred before, practically destroying one of the persons involved. (In fact, Sutter's Mill gold rush destroyed Colonel Sutter.) Jarbidge and the surrounding area might have remained wilderness had there been no gold discovery.

Kitty Wilkins lived during the days when Southeastern Oregon, Northern Nevada and Southwestern Idaho teemed with wild horses. The fleet-footed wild animals belonged to anyone who caught and branded them. So Kitty and John, who were very fine riders and judges of horses, organized a group of bronc riders. Kitty hired and fired the riders, some of whom were rough, hard characters. She ruled them and they respected her; any time a rider did not obey orders he was dismissed.

Among Kitty's riders were some famous men, such as Jess Coates, who rode before the King and Queen of England at a command performance; Walter Scott, later known as Death Valley Scotty; and Hugo Strickland, many times winner of the world champion bronc rider crown. The other four Strickland boys were fine riders also, and for several years Lee Strickland was foreman of the Wilkins' outfit.

Kitty kept spreading their territory until the range and the Wilkins' Ranches were among the largest and best known in the West. She rode a side saddle and wore the usual feminine riding skirt of those days. Kitty rode with her men much of the time. She thought and talked horse talk, bred horses, sold them and knew the good ones from the bad ones.

Technically, a wild horse is a tame horse gone wild, or an untamed descendant. The first Spaniards brought horses into North America and the early explorers found them here. The Indians used the horses, and didn't castrate them so the animals multiplied.

Jack knew wild horses did not always live where it was green and there was a supply of water. He saw them survive in barren desert countries, on top of ridges or over rocky open flats in Wyoming. Horses can smell water. If there is a hidden spring a mile or two away, they will find it. The mustangs were remarkable animals, tough and fast — and a spectacular sight running together, their long manes and tails flying.

A wild stallion would lure a ranch mare from a corral, whinnying as if calling 'come live a free life with me.' Of course some ranchers did not want the wild horse to multiply enticing his mares away; then too, the rancher knew the animals congregated by hundreds on the hillsides — fed too close on the bunch grass or pawed away the snow and dug out the roots. This would ruin the area for cattle grazing, and sometimes the grass would be replaced by sagebrush.

Unlike the cattle ranchers, Kitty and her men took pride in the wild mustangs and gathered them to break or to breed. They had many ways in which to catch them. After a trap corral was built in a box canyon and v-shaped wings built out one-half mile, the horses were driven into the corral. Or a trap was built gradually around their water hole — gradually, so the horses became accustomed to the new parts added each day. After they were in the corral, someone hiding near the entrance closed the gate. There were other ways but these were the methods used more generally by the Idaho and Nevada ranchers.

Jack Goodwin's curiosity about this remarkable Kitty Wilkins and her horse ranch took him to visit Mr. Roland Hawes, who, with his family, moved to the Three Creek area from the Bruneau Valley. Jack asked Roland if he had known the woman, the Horse Queen.

"Yes," said Hawes, "Let me tell you about a chance meeting we had with the pretty lady, Kitty.

"One day my father, my uncle Will Turner, Fred Belnap (a man working for my father) and I were working with the Wilkins' outfit, gathering a bunch of horses on the desert. The animals had been in the Winter Camp and Crow's Nest; they were part Wilkins' horses and part ours, of course we had less than they had. We were trying to put them in next to a rimrock so as to cut out a few saddle broke horses from the wild ones. There was a horse in there dragging a riata, which had not been on the horse's neck long, as it was still in good shape. It turned out that one of Kitty's men had roped his horse some day before and it had gotten away with his lariat. Kitty had ten or twelve men working with her at that time.

"It's a Rule of the Range that if there is a wild horse out there with a riata and you are a good cowboy and can get the rope it is yours. Belnap was riding a good horse and he roped the wild one. With a little help, Fred choked the horse down and got the rope off. We finished gathering horses and went back to Bruneau to have them get our camp and supplies ready.

"You see, our family, that is the Hawes family, had been losing so many cattle in the Bruneau Valley, and the Three Creek area with its new range and lots of room looked good to my father, so we were moving to Three Creek.

32

"In short order we had the wagon and supplies ready. Fred Belnap was with us. We came to Winter Camp the first day and were going to camp down on the river in the little cabin there. It wasn't far down, but the road was rough. Just before we went down, we saw a big dust coming from the inside desert. (We call it that because it is between the forks of Clover Creek and the big Bruneau). It was the Wilkins' outfit coming; they had gathered between three hundred and four hundred horses and colts. They were going to brand colts and were bringing them into the canyon where they could hold them. Then they would work those horses and brand the colts, a job that might take two or three days.

"So we just camped on top of the hill. As I remember, my mother and I slept in a little tent and my father and Fred slept under the wagon.

"Belnap took a bucket and rode down to get some water for the camp. He rode right past this little cabin where the Wilkins' were camped. He rode over to the river and dipped up a bucket of water; when he went by the cabin one man came out, with not a 'Hello' or any greeting and said, 'Belnap, I hear you got my rope and I want it.'

"Belnap said, 'I took that rope off that horse and I am going to keep it.' So the fellow reached up and was going to try to pull Belnap off of his horse and he hit him over the head with that bucket of water and came riding up the hill. Belnap never said anything to my mother or father, just unrolled his bed and got his six-shooter out and put it on. He still had his empty bucket so he went down and got another bucket of water and no one tried to stop him that time. After he returned he told the family the story.

"Well, as the evening went on, Kitty came up to our camp. She said, 'Joe, we don't want any hard feelings between these two men, you had better tell Fred to give Jim back his rope.' But, my father said, 'Kitty, that is up to those two and has nothing to do with me.' They visited a short while and then she went back down to the cabin.

"Belnap said nothing more about it, but he kept the riata. I remember that night, my mother slept very little because she thought that fellow Jim would come up and not know in the dark which was father or Belnap sleeping under the wagon. She tried to get father to persuade Fred to give the riata back."

Jack had listened and knew Roland would never forget that meeting, even though he had been only a boy. Kitty must be quite a woman, thought Jack.

Kitty's great black stallion, Big Dave, ran free on Dave Island with his band of mares. Slim Walsh told Jack he rode horseback over that way one day looking for two horses that had strayed away from his packing camp.

"I heard a wild-soundin' whinny — almost like a scream — off in the distance," said Slim. "Along the ridge was this black mustang stallion, with his large, handsome head held high. He was rearing and screaming and tossing his head as if he was the king and the mares had to do as he bid. And they did too, or else he nipped them with his sharp teeth and sent them running where he wanted them."

Slim didn't go too close because he had heard that Big Dave had been known to race with teeth bared and hooves flying toward another horse entering his island.

By the year of 1919, when the First World War was over, the horse ranges were gone and so were the horse markets. The development and irrigation projects took over the boundless spaces where the beautiful wild horses ran with the velocity of the wind. The automobile came into our way of life, also the large cattle ranches, and since the mustangs were believed to be a menace to the range they were mercilessly hunted down by planes, or any way, just to be sold and slaughtered for pet food.

It was then that Kitty Wilkins, still the Queen, young at heart, sold her ranches and horses and semi-retired to her home in Glensferry, Idaho. She was always interested in the progress of the nation and kept a small ranch in Glensferry until she passed away October, 1936.

A search of the available records yields no verdict in the case of Laura Kitty Wilkins vs. C.C. Logan. Very likely the dispute was settled out of court, with Kitty receiving an undisclosed consideration in exchange for her claim to the property. What is certain is that the Hot Hole became a stop-over for travelers going to Jarbidge. A permanent log building with sleeping rooms on the second floor accommodate the visitors; a swimming pool and three small bathrooms catch the hot spring water for those who want to bathe or swim. Fishing became a good sport in the East Fork River and deer hunters go to the Wilkins' Island to hunt deer and not to round-up mustangs.

CHAPTER 7

One clear, spring morning Jack started packing for a prospecting trip. He had the unfortunate experience with horses falling down the mountainside when he went before, but that was in the winter — the warmer days had melted most of the snow and he wouldn't take any risks. The dream of riches to be picked up in the barely explored high country above Jarbidge was ever present in his mind and he couldn't resist the urge. He would go now. The family would be coming to Jarbidge in a couple of months, besides he had lots of road work to do as soon as he got back.

He saddled the roan horse to ride and was packing the sorrel with supplies. I've always wanted to pan and prospect the East Fork of the Jarbidge River, Jack thought as he kept on packing the alforjas on the pack-saddle. Only be gone a few days, but will tell Beadle where I'm going.

He loaded a coffee pot, skillet and other camp cooking utensils, some canned beans, flour, salt, coffee and slab bacon. Then he put his bedroll of three blankets on the top and a small pick and axe, covered it all with a canvas tarpaulin and secured the pack with a rope tied into a diamond hitch. He slipped his 30-30 Winchester rifle into the scabbard on his saddle. Over the saddle horn he slung the strap of the leather case which held his field glass.

As Jack picked up the lead rope on the pack animal and mounted his horse, he told Beadle not to worry. He would be back in a few days.

"Going up to the little, spring-fed lake which is the head of the Jarbidge River, then over the ridge by Cougar Peak and down into East Fork. I hope I can find the Howard Cabin and come out there at the north end of the Jarbidge District."

Beadle bid him good luck and a good trip.

"Be careful, Jack see you in a few days."

The trail, after a mile or so, became faint. Visible only to eyes skilled in such reading, an occasional hoof-print, crushed grass, a small stone dislodged — these spoke mutely. Soon he found only a deer trail to follow. When the canyon and riverside became too choked with willows and groves of pale-barked aspen, he climbed along the side of the steep mountain, sometimes crossing loose gray shale that slipped and slid under the horses' hoofs.

When he had ridden a couple of miles, Jack stopped, looked and felt the vastness of the mountains. The sun shone brilliantly, the sky was a deep blue, the mountains were a bluish-purple. He was small compared to the masses of granite, the peaks towering over the canyon and the forest, yet he was also bigger. They stood unmoving, unthinking, but he could move and think and speak when he chose.

Peaks left to right: Jarbidge Peak, Black Jumbo, Square Top, Matterhorn, and Cougar Peak.

Jack had entered the forest of balsam fir, spruce and limber pine trees which soared magnificently into the sky. As he rode down toward the stream, he could hear the rush of a falls in the distance. Shortly he came upon the creek which spread itself into a sheet film, a thin crystal spray over the dark rocks, then tumbled a hundred feet into a foamy pool. Boulders, smooth with the constant beat of the falls, edged the pool and the foam formed the most delicate and lacy frills along the sandy edges of the boulders.

Everywhere he went the dainty tracks of deer were ahead of him. All morning long he rode through dense timberland, over fallen trees, sharp stones and around boulders, up and down such steep declines that the horses were almost on their haunches. He often stopped to rest the animals. As he crossed the stream, it got smaller and smaller until it was a narrow brook coming out of the lake.

Now the rider halted and looked upon the meadow just below and around the small Jarbidge Lake. He watched some ruffed grouse feeding. The male was strutting up and down a log, drumming with his stout wings and looking about to see if he had the hen's attention. The bird held his head high and crest raised and the dark blue-green ruff glistened above his neck. The handsome black-banded tail was spread in a fan. Rump, a-rump, ka-thump, it was mating season. The grouse saw a stranger entering their habitat and, like a whirlwind, they burst into the air.

Jack's sharp eyes caught a flash of gray fur run into a thicket. That would be a coyote trying to creep close enough to catch one of the grouse. A rockchuck caught the flash of gray too, and he slid from his lookout and with a last defiant whistle, disappeared into his hole in the ground.

It was after lunchtime so Jack dismounted. He dropped the reins, loosened the cinches, and watched the horses as they fed on the tender grass of the meadow. He

36

opened a can of pork and beans and unwrapped the meat sandwich he had prepared that morning. Probably before he got back he would be lunching on jerky, of which he brought a sufficient amount.

As he sat, life was everywhere around him. Little chipmunks darted about seeking buds and tender stems. The larger golden mantle sat up with his little forepaws draped over his round belly. Watching — maybe the man would leave a few crumbs for him.

After a half-hour of rest, nourishment and water, Jack caught his horses, mounted and started on. The lake edges were spongy with the run-off of a nearby snowbank which he avoided by easing around the end of it. Soon he came to a narrow, rough section where he knew it was too dangerous to stay mounted. So he slipped off and tied the rope of the pack horse to the tail of his roan then led him.

When he reached the pass, he was surprised that he could see for miles. He slid his field glass from the case and peered along the high, rugged ridge of peaks which rose at an altitude of between over 10,000 to 11,000 feet and lay between Jarbidge River and the East Fork of the Jarbidge River. He had climbed nearly 5,000 feet from the Jarbidge River Canyon and was looking down into the East Fork River Canyon, which he estimated dropped away another 5,000 feet. To the South he could distinguish Cougar and Mary's Peaks, and to the North were Matterhorn, Square Top, Black Jumbo and then the Jarbidge Peak.

Jack saw a pair of eagles gliding in the sky. Since there was a pair, there must be a nest somewhere, so he looked for a jutting rim of a pinnacle and followed it down to a shelf where he could see part of a platform made of sticks and limbs with a few tufts of grass showing. High enough from the ground for protection from predators and far enough below the mesa to insure safety from above was the eyrie with no shade from the cliff for it and only one scraggly tree growing on the shelf. But eagles do not want their young sheltered from rain and sun, and also they need a good, wide-open platform on which to land.

The larger of the circling eagles, which must be the female, had a wingspread of nearly eight feet. She dived toward a thicket-covered slope and as she came closer in his vision, he saw her bright, orange-yellow feet, armed with curved, deadly talons and scythelike beak of the same color. She was a golden eagle and a fierce, bold huntress with keener eyesight than a human. The bird dropped from sight as she neared the slope. In a matter of minutes she appeared again, flying swiftly toward the eyrie. As her wings and tail fanned out to check her speed, Jack could see the white on her tail feathers with the broad, black band — feathers the Indians collected years ago to make their warbonnets.

She landed gently on the platform which served as cradle, dining table, landing strip and gymnasium for the eaglets while they stayed there over twelve weeks to grow strong enough to survive by their own efforts. Jack, looking through the field glass, saw the mother drop a ground squirrel and a down-covered head appear.

He thought it about time to camp for the night, so untied the rope from the roan's tail and eased himself into the saddle. He dropped gingerly down a game trail that led to a beautiful spot, Emerald Lake. Then he unpacked the sorrel and took the saddle and bridle from his roan. After watering the horses at the lake, he hobbled both and attached a bell around the roan's neck. Most likely they would graze close by because the grass was abundant.

Next Jack gathered some wood and built a small fire. He cut a springy willow pole, attached a line and wet fly baited with a small insect and tossed the hook into the crystalline waters of the lake. Within a few minutes he had enough delicious trout for his dinner.

The brown pine needles were soft underfoot and would provide a mattress for his bed. He kicked out the rocks on level ground then spread the horse blankets down and a small blanket on top. The other blankets of the bedroll and the canvas he used for covers. The saddle served as a fair pillow — a little high, but Jack was one who could make the best of any circumstance.

The moon came out so clear and close that he felt he could almost touch it. He heard the laughing yap of coyotes and knew mountain lions could be watching from some high rim. Although you seldom see them, even in the daylight, they are there.

The next morning the sun came up suddenly, spilling like a pot of gold paint over the pale blue sky. The water on the lake shimmered as gusts of wind slid across it. It would be a warm day. There was hope, Jack thought, of a mountain sprinkle of rain to save the grass from browning and dying and keep the wild flowers alive and fragrant.

The golden eagles, the proud and fearless birds, were hunting again this morning. Jack saw them in the air as he was cooking his breakfast.

The horses were only a few hundred yards away so he caught them and after breakfast he packed up and worked down to the river. He followed the East Fork panning the fine gravel. The *color* which he recovered in the panning process was an indication that it must have come from above as float (pieces of surface ore which washed into the river from the hillside or came down one of the tributaries). Jack saw some jutting outcrops on the hillside, so he climbed up toward the high ground. He found some quartz with silver-gray streaks which carried silver and gold. Time did not permit checking all the streams and hillsides, nevertheless he was satisfied there was gold in that region; and he took two small sample sacks of the gravel and rock specimens to assay when he got to the office.

Just before Jack got to where Slide Creek entered the river some magpies flew up from a willow patch. Upon riding to the spot, he found the fresh carcass of a doe, almost covered with sticks and leaves that a lion had scraped up from all sides to hide its kill. It had ripped open the belly and removed the stomach and intestines, which lions never eat, but had eaten the liver, heart and kidneys. This lion had recently been there and had eaten some of the hind quarter. From all indications the doe had been suckling a fawn which, being left alone in that wilderness, would not last long. Jack camped for the night, preparing his camp and tying his horses in an open place so he would be ready in case the lion came back. At dawn the lion returned to his kill and made another meal off of it and just as it was leaving the covered remains of the doe, Jack shot the lion.

He shot him through the heart so as not to spoil the skull. A lucky shot, Jack told himself, and a beautiful specimen. After a short wait to make sure the animal was not merely wounded, he walked over to find that it was a large male. The animal had a large, round head with gray markings, reddish-yellow sides, slightly darker back and snow-white belly. What a nice hide it would make for a rug in Hattie's and his new home he was going to build. He carefully skinned his prize and wrapped the pelt to pack with his outfit on the horse.

Before leaving Jack looked carefully in the willows for the fawn, but never found it. So he proceeded down the river and prospected as he went.

"What's that?" said Jack thinking aloud. "Lo and Behold! A huge snowslide has come down and crossed the river."

Keeping in its course down the narrow canyon, the river had eroded the slide and made a tunnel through the twenty feet deep snowslide. If he kept to the stream bed, the opening was wide and tall enough for Jack to ride his horse through and lead the pack horse. Drippings from the arch fell on him as he rode through. Boulders and tree branches were visible hanging precariously in the snow above.

Jack had done well, eaten fish, grouse and had plenty of jerked venison left. He rode on down the river to a gravel bar where he stayed the last night out. The next morning he took to the trail up the mountain and out of the canyon, passed Howard's Cabin in the forest. From there he headed towards Mahoney Ranger's Station and into Jarbidge, arriving there in the early evening.

CHAPTER 8

The cold winter and heavy snows in Salt Lake City depressed Hattie, but most of all the realization she would be separated from Jack for so many months. She had been treated kindly at his sisters' and mother's homes yet they had many children and did not need the extra company. Hattie often overheard remarks and became uncomfortable, sometimes breaking out in tears. Also, that Jack's letters were slow coming from the new camp made her unhappy. Then there was the day when Gracie came to her sobbing.

"Mamma, I want to tell you something."

"What is it, Dear?" Hattie held her little girl close, what could possibly be the matter now?

"I swallowed a pin, Mamma," the child replied in a frightened voice. Hattie anxiously had Grace show her what size the pin was among the ones stuck in the pin cushion.

"This one with the big white head," Grace cried.

Hattie called the doctor and he gave her instructions. It was difficult to keep her child of three and one-half years from water or any liquid for a day and a night. That special diet of solids that the doctor had ordered — when Gracie called out, "I want some water, Mamma," all she could give her was a teaspoonful. When the pin passed they were all relieved. Hattie knew she must go on, so she packed, said goodbyes to Jack's relatives, and left the next day for Kansas City.

Instead of going to live with her older sister, Hattie rented a little house in Kansas City, Kansas. She sent for her youngest sister, Pearl.

Pearl had a natural aptitude for drama and enjoyed traveling around the States, taking lead parts in stock plays. She was a beautiful, young woman and extremely captivated by the theatrical life.

Dear Pearlie was too busy to get married, thought Hattie, even though she was twenty-two. She would be good company, and because Pearl had been with her older sisters when some of their children were born, she could help Hattie.

When Pearl received Hattie's letter, she made immediate plans to join her.

Jack followed the reports of the Bourne mineral values and knew they had been exaggerated. Therefore, he was not surprised when, in May, people started leaving

40

Jarbidge District, criticizing the country as they went. However, when the snow had melted, many ledges of good ore were found and discoveries made daily which provided promising and substantial results.

With the opening of spring and the extension of the road from Wilkins' Ranch, passengers and freight were delivered into the camp. This reduced the price of merchandise and supplies for the prospectors and the businessmen. The Bourne Mine group was financed and some mill machinery came in by freight.

Jack and Beadle felt a fresh surge of optimism when a Guggenheim representative came to the camp to inspect the facilities for mining and milling.

Jarbidge Post Office was established the 5th of March of the year of 1910, with Roy M. Nail postmaster. Then Winthrop Fisk took over the office the 5th of July, 1912, and Mr. John S. Fleming was appointed the 7th of May of 1913, keeping the appointment until his wife succeeded him in 1922.

Jack always had time to write to his wife and baby:

"I received your loving and welcome letter of May 8th, and I know we have a boy by this time, as I was dreaming about you and him last night. I am praying for you and hope you have an easy time and a fine boy, don't you?

"If you are tired of reading my three letters a week, just say so. I can write one a week, but all the pleasure I have is writing to you and I would just as soon write every mail day as not.

"In the camp I counted two hundred eighteen tents and there are as many more scattered over the hills around. They want me to work on the road to Charleston, but the weather is too bad now. I have one good claim staked and will get more when the snow melts.

"I tell you, Grace will have a fine time with the new baby. It will tickle her. Take good care of yourself and our Baby, don't take any chances. Be patient and I will rustle hard so that we can always be together. It is lonesome for me when it is snowing and I have to stay in the tent. I have to fix my shoes tonight.

"Write often. Your loving lonesome Jack.

"P.S. Please send a stamped envelope with each letter. Such things are hard to find here."

By the next letter from Hattie, Jack learned that he was the father of a new baby girl. Although he had been hoping for a boy, he was very proud and wrote to Hattie:

"Take good care of yourself and Baby Goldie. Thank Doctor Seright and Nurse Headly, also thank Pearl for administering the chloroform to you before the nurse came. I'll be anxious to see you and the dolls."

There was always a P.S. on Jack's many letters . . .

"Hattie dear, would you like a rock house or canvas? Canvas is plentiful. There is no lumber unless we cut logs out of the forest."

Hattie had quite a different idea about the name for her new baby girl. She had already named her, and not Goldie. Hattie was gaining strength fast and would be joining her husband soon. She was worried about his taking those dangerous prospecting trips.

"Now! Was Jack kidding about no lumber for a house? No! No! Not another canvas tenthouse . . ." She passed it off and remembered how Jack liked to tell those wild stories in his humorous way.

It was early morning the first of July, 1910, when the Oregon Short Line train pulled into Hollister, Idaho. Hattie Goodwin gathered up her valise and handbag, and just then the conductor came along.

"Don't be in a hurry, lady. I will take these for you," he said, smiling. "You will have plenty to take care of with those two little ones."

Grace had her nose pushed against the window looking for her Papa as the faded yellow depot came into view. Hattie carefully wrapped the blanket around her six-weeks-old baby Helen and sat waiting for the train to stop and for her husband to come aboard.

Hollister was hardly a town, with only three makeshift buildings edging a board sidewalk. There were some freight wagons and buckboards with horses tied to a hitching rail in front of the depot.

"I wonder if they are waiting for passengers and freight from this train," whispered Hattie. There was Jack hurrying to the train entrance steps. What a handsome, sun-tanned man, she thought, and how happy she was to see him. Her two children had blonde hair like his, although it was difficult to say what the baby's might be later.

"God," he said, almost smothering her in kisses and a big hug. "It's good to see you – I thought you'd never get here – been waiting for this day so long." He wanted to see the new baby, and all the while Gracie was tugging at his arm. So he scooped up both children in one big affectionate hug, because this was 'his day.'

As Jack helped his wife off the train he said, "Why, you look just like a city gal – the other women will be jealous of your pretty outfit." Hattie knew that her new linen suit had cost too much, and she hadn't been able to resist the leghorn hat caught up on one side with a trimming of cornflowers to show off her hair, so it was a relief to know that he admired her outfit. When they headed for the high-sided Bain freight wagon with the spring seats, she knew her garb was impractical and a bit out of place, so she changed to a sunbonnet which she got from a small satchel.

The wagon could accommodate a driver and three passengers on its two seats, while carrying freight in the bottom of the wagon and back of the seats. Taking all into consideration, Jack had made it as comfortable as he could for his family.

As the vehicles jolted along the dusty road, the morning air became warm with the rising sun. Occasionally a jackrabbit darted from behind a clump of bushes, or a rockchuck ambled out of the road and into his hole. Sagebrush blanketed the low-lying hills as far as one could see.

They had come over eight miles from the railroad station when, quite suddenly, the travelers reached the deep canyon where the Salmon Falls Creek flowed along the rugged, twisting bottom.

In 1909 and 1910, the Salmon Dam had been erected by the Twin Falls Salmon River Land and Water Company. A narrow roadway built on top of the dam let the wagons and traffic cross. However, the approaches had not been cut through the column of rock when the Goodwins came that way, so they used the old wooden bridge above the dam.

The rigs passed ranch houses where meadows of hay were soon to be cut and stacked. Wild iris grew along the small streams that meandered through the

44

meadows. The ranches had names such as Cedar Creek, where Grandma Brackett had lived and now the Clark family resided; House Creek, Devil Creek, Three Creek and Flat Creek Ranch where the Hodge family homesteaded and built the two story log cabin many years before.

The immigrants stopped now and then at a ranch to refresh themselves and the horses. The cluster of log rooms that had heretofore been the humble ranch of Jerome Helsley were crowded to the limit during the rush to the Jarbidge gold camp. The granary and sheds had also been turned into sleeping quarters, where the hardened traveler could throw his bedroll down and not complain of a close room. All along the route the farm houses were busy taking care of the invading gold seekers, but the busiest places were the Three Creek settlement and Logan's restaurant and lodgings at Kitty Wilkins' Hot Springs Camp.

At Three Creek Thomas Higgins owned a store and saloon. He had purchased about $8,000 worth of provisions and miner's stock for his store in order to supply the miners as well as have a good supply for the nearby ranchers.

Jeff and Lenny Hamilton had cabins, tents and an eating house for the freighters, prospectors and those who needed lodging and food. The overnight accommodations were usually filled to capacity. As it had been a long, hot journey that day, the family stopped at Three Creek for the night.

In later years, Mr. Roland Hawes told of a childhood experience at this Three Creek settlement . . .

"I came there to Tom Higgins' store with my father when I was a little boy. It happened to be the fourth of July and it seemed that all the buckaroos in the country were there that day. There must have been nearly twenty-five men and horses there. Things were pretty lively. The saloon was in one end of the stone building. The boys got drunk and went outside, threw bottles into the air and shot at them with pistols, then they would laugh and shout. It made quite an impression on me.

"My father bought a round of drinks for the fellows and bought the supplies that we came for and we left. Maybe, if I had not been with him he would have stayed awhile.

"Also, I remember the little log hotel just below the store, off down in the cottonwood trees. The owner had a pretty good sized barn and every spring if the baled hay was all sold out he would have a dance or two in there. It would be an old fashioned barn dance. But, of course, if the hay was not about sold he was afraid of fire."*

The Goodwins awoke early to resume their trip and after another eleven miles arrived at the Rimrock where they could overlook the activities at Kitty Wilkins' Hot Hole Camp. The makeshift road was very rocky and steep coming off the Rimrock and going down into the camp. Some freight wagons were changing their heavy loads to pack mules. However, some passenger wagons forded the East Fork of the Jarbidge River and pulled out and up the steep road to the large Wilkins' Island.

After reaching the top, the road followed the tableland for a few miles and the going was much easier. Next came Rattlesnake Way Station, built and operated by Rattlesnake Jack. At this station there were as many as ten wagonloads of outfits waiting to be transported by pack train into the camp, taking supplies and machinery to the mines. The charges were six cents per pound for freight and five dollars for the use of a saddle horse. It was here that freighters could change horses or mules from the many animals in the corral, which numbered at times as many as one hundred. A blacksmith, Mr. A.J. Lund, arrived there with his tools and was needed so badly that he stayed to work awhile before going into Jarbidge.

Some of the freighters had their own relief horses there. Since Jarbidge had no stables and very little feed, a few of the freighters unloaded their supplies in the camp and returned to the station where they had feed and rest for their animals. Also, it was here that a five hundred pound tent was packed on a thirteen hundred pound mule. The tent was to house the Bear Creek Saloon.

The way station had a saloon, rooms and food for men and their families, so that was the best place to spend the second night. In the opposite end of the building from the saloon was a huge rock fireplace. After dinner the family sat looking into the fire watching the curling flames engulf the pine logs. Hattie held the baby and Gracie sat on her Papa's lap. One more day and the trip would be over, but now they would relax at the warm fireplace.

Men came and went and their heavy boots scraped the wooden floor. The loud talking at the bar penetrated Hattie's thoughts.

A large but well dressed man, apparently gay and flushed with drink, came staggering in the door singing in a loud voice — "Buffalo Gal, Are You Coming Out Tonight . . . and Dance By The Light Of The Moon." He staggered headlong into a bystander who seized him and steadied him on his feet. He thanked the man and advanced to the bar.

---

*Mr. Roland Hawes, whose family were ranchers of Bruneau Valley and Three Creek, Idaho, in private conversation with the author.

"Champagne!" he shouted grandly. "For everyone."

The barkeeper frowned. "We don't handle none of them fancy boozes. Anyway, you likely couldn't pay for it even if we had it."

The large man stood proudly. "You insult me, I'm from Denver and I got lots of money. Going into that gold camp to do some promoting — if I can ever get there in this Godforsaken country."

He turned and started to stalk out of the place with great dignity, but did not make it to the door. His knees suddenly caved in and he collapsed on the floor.

A man nearby, probably a friend, pulled him up trying to get him on his feet, but failed, so slung the big man over his shoulder and walked out of the station.

The Goodwins' lunch stop on the journey was Jack Hole where Mr. and Mrs. Baty operated the lodginghouse. A few tent-buildings had been erected and a new strike made in that district too. Jack Hole was where the Jack and Jenny Creeks merged into one roaring and fast moving tributary to soon empty into the Jarbidge River in the canyon far below.

It was here that Jack asked James and George Crisp to help him with his family, wagon and team. Jim and George, better known as the "Crisp Twins" had ridden or tramped these mountains and trails many times this past winter because they located and developed eighteen claims in the Jack Creek Crater.

As the wagons rumbled and were eased down the slope between willows and trees, to plunge their wheels into the swift but narrow Jack Creek, slipping on the rocks and churning up the soft, shifting bottom, the men whipped and cursed to keep the teams moving across and up the steep bank. Then came the long pull out of the canyon, along Jenny Creek, to a switchback and up to the top. For wagons loaded with supplies or heavy mine machinery, the four-to-ten-horse teams strained in the harness, their lathered flanks heaving. The men often ran alongside, urging the horses or mules, or chunking the wheels when they reached a near level place to give the animals time to rest or blow.

Sometimes the teams were doubled, leaving the other wagon beside the road to return to later. The long string of horses pulling, with bellies near the ground and nostrils flaring, were floundering for footing on the sliding rocks and loose gravel, sometimes taking to the side of the road in the sagebrush. If the animals were balky and there was doubt they would make the last eighth of a mile of steep grade, the drivers asked for one final plunge under skinning lashes of the whip and extreme bellowing. Then came the stop of played-out horses and their long rest before the men had to gather up the lines for the next mile of nearly flat rutted road to cottonwood springs. In the meantime, the freighters rubbed a sagging hip or two, eased galling collars or patted a lowered neck, loosening the lathered mane.

After spitting out their tobacco and wiping their parched lips on a sleeve or the back of a sunburned hand, men drank from the water bag. If someone had a bottle of whiskey he would offer a drink and usually they would empty it and sorrowfully toss the bottle into the brush beside the road. And talk about "what's for supper at Mrs. Fritz' restaurant — a good night's rest at The Nevada Hotel, or a poker game at the Bear Bar; or maybe a jaunt down to the lower end of town to see the 'girls.' "

"We are only a mile from the camp, now, Mrs. Goodwin," said Jim Crisp, as he saw the terrified expression Hattie tried to conceal. She was weary, hot and dusty; and apprehension had taken a toll of the young woman with her precious family.

The road down Moore's Gulch, to arrive in the canyon, was steep enough to amaze a mountain goat. Besides rough-locking both rear wheels, the men chained a log to drag behind the rear axle. Even so, the wagon ran ahead and crowded the horses. Jack thought it better that Jim carry the baby and Hattie and Gracie walk. Gracie was crying and Hattie knew she was frightened. She tried to console her little girl.

Jim Crisp told people years later that it was part of the folklore that he carried the first tiny baby into the Jarbidge Mining Camp.

By the Author: I have since looked over this now seldom-used road, still rugged, steep and treacherous; used mainly by fourwheel drive vehicles — and pondered how little it has changed.

What could have been in the heart and soul of a young woman, my Mamma, as she brought her two daughters into this frightening pioneer life. There must have been courage and inspiration, but most of all the love for her husband, father of her children.

Such was the fortitude of many women and children coming into this camp or any new town of the little known West.

CHAPTER 10

The evening of July 2, 1910, when she arrived in Jarbidge, Hattie wasn't aware of the beauty of the untamed mountains which lifted high above the dark green stretches of graceful pine and the lighter green of aspen and cottonwood. She didn't see the rosy, rock cliffs which spired upward and the sun touch the rock masses of the canyon walls, as the family carefully found their way into the prospectors' and miners' paradise.

She was only concerned about Gracie's crying and about coming into this new gold camp. She hoped it would not be a merciless wilderness, too rough for her and for her two little girls. For her — she could endure it, even Grace could — but what about the six-weeks-old baby? Hattie worried, but never spoke.

When they reached the canyon floor, Jack helped Hattie and Gracie into the wagon and Jim passed the sleeping baby, which was carefully wrapped in blankets, into Hattie's arms. They had walked only a short way, but Hattie was exhausted, her feet hurt, her once lovely linen suit was wrinkled and dusty. The front of it was soiled where Helen spit-up when she was nursing.

Jack sensed the anguish Hattie was experiencing so before starting the horses again, he slipped his arms around her waist drawing her closer as she rested her head on his shoulder.

"Well, Sweetheart, we are in Jarbidge, our new home." Jack didn't ask her how she liked it from the view on the hillside; this was not the time to ask that question.

When Hattie had regained her composure Jack withdrew his arms, picked up the reins and gave them a light flip and said, "Get up!"

In spite of all, Hattie swallowed hard and tried to keep back the tears of disillusionment. She envisioned the early weeks in Goldfield, the privations and lonely days in Happy Creek and Hart. Then her thoughts changed to her husband beside her and how they loved one another; she knew how capable he was and how this life pleased him. She remembered the quotation she had once read — "In the wilderness, part of the fascination lies in the unexpected."

Ahead of the team of horses, tents were visible along the roadside and river banks. The sun had left the canyon as the family arrived at Jimmy Cameron's Hotel, a large tent, where Jack had made arrangements to stay overnight, until they could get to

Pavlak by horseback. The street was crowded with men, many groups talking of the occurrences of the day, others hurrying from tent to tent. There were long lines of heavily loaded freight wagons, which had just arrived, drawn by sweating teams of horses and mules. The animals stood resting while men unloaded various supplies to different business places.

Jarbidge consisted of one main street flanked by tents and a few board and log cabins. Bear Creek coming out of the meadows near Bear Creek Summit and winding down its deep ravine, merged with the Jarbidge River at the center of town. Tents were erected on each side of the creek, giving the narrow roads the names, Bear Creek South and Bear Creek North. Any man who could handle a saw and hammer found employment putting up new buildings, log or tent frames, which gave both sides of the dusty, rutty road the crude semblance of a main street. There were general mercantile stores, restaurants, hotels, saloons and other establishments. A respectable distance from the business district and set apart at the lower end of town, stood the inevitable shacks and tents where the prostitutes set up business.

The next day as they rode along the trail which followed the edge of the river for two miles from Jarbidge to Pavlak, Hattie was amazed to see so many tents and diggings. Jack had a gentle horse for her as she carried the baby in her arms and Gracie rode behind the saddle.

The new home was a large framed tent with a wooden floor. The July days were warm, but Hattie wondered about the nights at 7000 feet elevation. The tent was equipped with an iron cook stove which Hattie scraped and polished, a homemade table and bench and two nondescript chairs, including a low rocker. A necessary screen door kept out the flies and mosquitos. The bed was wooden and supported a rather thin mattress. A cot and baby bed completed the bedroom, which was a canvas partitioned-off corner of the tent.

There was little to choose from at the store in Jarbidge but canned foods. Nevertheless, Hattie could make the plainest fare into a very tasty dish. By suppertime the tent smelled appetizingly of hot baking-powder biscuits and other goodies.

50

Jack hugged Hattie affectionately and remarked, "You've made it feel homelike already, Sweetheart, seems like it's been ages since I've eaten your good cooking. I wanted you to wait until you were stronger and I had a house built for you, but now I'm glad you came. Are you feeling all right?"

"Oh, yes! I feel fine and I'm glad we came as soon as we could. I missed you terribly and I know Gracie is so happy to be with you again." Hattie smiled and blushed happily and her hazel eyes glistened in the lamplight.

Soon Hattie Goodwin felt at home in her tent house. Game was plentiful and she knew how to prepare it. She always had a pot of steaming coffee and a dessert for the company who came to visit. From her visitors she learned about the very early residents of Pavlak, why and how they came there.

Mr. and Mrs. John Swicegood built a cabin and ran the Hub settlement at Pine Creek which was near the Goodwins and they became good friends. Judge and Mrs. Yewell and their two boys built a nice home across the river. The mining settlement of Pavlak, Nevada, was someday to be a memory to the residents who lived there and the men who worked the mines.

Author's note — To my knowledge, there has, since the discovery of Pavlak, never been a factual article written about the small community and its people.

CHAPTER 11

Hattie stood in the doorway of the tent home and watched Jack as he rode the bay horse along the trail by the river which led to the steep and rocky mine trail. She watched him until he was out of sight in the mahogany trees. He seemed so self-confident and strong. He was in his element among these rugged mountains. To him the rocks and earth made a kind of fantastic puzzle to be explored for gold and silver — rocks to be crushed and panned and earth to be opened and tunneled and timbered to its depths. Oddly enough, Hattie would rather think about preparing the soil for flowers and vegetable plants — perhaps a garden. Surely they would talk about the cabin to be built while the weather was warm and have it completed by the first turning of the cottonwood trees along the river. Autumn came fast in the mountains and then winter was there before one realized.

Now he was gone, no longer in sight, and Hattie was left to contemplate the morning work. Lonely sounds broke the silence, among them a robin perched in the nearby cottonwood tree by the river singing its familiar song. She turned back into the tent, grateful to hear the baby-chatter of her two little girls while Gracie was playing with the baby. Much to do today, thought Hattie. The groceries and canned goods which they had packed from Jarbidge must be stored away; also there was washing to be done for the children.

When Mr. Beadle visited them later in the day she would ask him about the meeting of the residents of the district which was to be held in Jarbidge tomorrow. He would know, thought Hattie, for Tom Beadle was a respectable man, a well mannered gentleman. I wonder why he has never married, pondered Hattie, and he loves children. At least, there is nothing he wouldn't do for our two girls.

The next day was warm and sunny and the Goodwin family rode horseback to Jarbidge. Jack was looking forward to the day when a road would be built so they could take the buggy instead of riding horseback. Many of the folks from Pavlak and the district would be at the meeting.

People had assembled in the office of the District Recorder to form an organization to promote the general interest of the Jarbidge Mining District. After considerable discussion, they decided to name this organization the Jarbidge Commercial Club. Seventeen members subscribed and paid an initiation fee of ten

52

dollars per person. They elected a president, vice president, secretary and treasurer. A committee of three was appointed by the president to draft a constitution and by-laws. Also five members were elected to act as a Board of Directors, of which Mr. Tom Beadle was one.

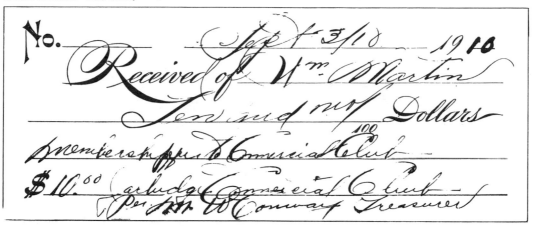

Within ten days the club had a charter membership of forty-eight men. The following committees were appointed: Dance, Building, Mail, Sanitation and Road. Three hundred and thirty dollars had been acquired in membership fees and fifty-two dollars was donated for a mail delivery fund. They adopted the Indian Ja-Ha-Bich design for their Club stationery.

The Sanitation Committee reported that the sheep which had been grazing on Pine Creek, Bear Creek and other creeks in the immediate vicinity of Jarbidge and Pavlak had left for other parts, thereby freeing the streams from any unsanitary conditions. Also, the committee presented a set of resolutions and rules notifying the residents of the camp of certain precautions to be taken against filth and governing the location of privies. Copies were posted in conscpicuous places throughout the district.

The Building Committee reported the promise of Tom Beadle's lot just south of his assay office in the middle of town, west side of the street, on which to erect a log building. It was suggested that every member of the club donate or furnish a certain amount of material or labor towards the construction.

At the meeting on August 27, 1910, Tom Beadle was refunded his membership fee in consideration for the lot he donated to the town for the building of the Jarbidge Commercial Clubhouse. And one week later the lot had been staked and plans drawn for the building, a log structure sixty feet long and twenty-three feet wide.

Logs were cut from the forest above town, snaked to the log slide down into Bear Creek and delivered to the lot for two dollars each. They were then hewed to measure about twenty-five feet.

Jack Goodwin was elected to engineer the road from Jarbidge to Pavlak: and thence out of the canyon by way of Charleston and on to Deeth, Nevada. The little town of Deeth, with a population of seven hundred energetic people raised five thousand dollars in one evening to construct a wagon road into Jarbidge. Deeth was on the railroad and wanted the freight business. Since Jack had a team of horses and a wagon and could hire other men and their teams, he promised he would survey and work on the new road as soon as he had his family settled and the weather permitted. However, nature was against this route because some months of the year heavy snowdrifts would make the road practically impassable.

Hattie visited with Mrs. Lund, the blacksmith's wife, while Jack attended the meetings. She would not be able to come every time, but she knew Jack could. Later, when their baby was a little older she would leave her with Mrs. Pavlak. Matilda Pavlak, the sister of David A. Bourne, said, "Hattie, any time you want to leave Helen with me, I'd rather take care of her than go to a party. Leave Gracie, too, I love children and you have such good little ones."

The weather grew colder as autumn came to the canyon. The chokecherries, elderberries, currants and other wild berries had ripened, ready for jelly-making. The streamsides and hillsides were splashed with red, gold and yellow-bronze, like dreams in a mellow haze. Hunters stalking deer above the canyon floor felt the bite of stinging winds that meant the snow was near at hand. Cones bristled from pines and seed grasses were bowed with their loads. The deer's reddish-tan coat had faded to a neutral grey.

Jack cut long logs in the forest. He brought in pine and spruce, some eight to ten inches thick in diameter, others not so large. After topping and limbing them, he snaked them down the log trail with the bay horse, Dick. His friends and a hired carpenter had soon finished a sturdy cabin of three rooms.

Hattie and Jack had chosen a beautiful cabinsite close to the river's edge and under large cottonwood trees. There was plenty of room for barns, chicken pens and gardens back of the house. To cross the river and get to the trail to Jarbidge, they built a footbridge.

Jack's team of horses were good work animals. The bay could be ridden and was gentle enough for Hattie to ride with the children, but the grey was not. Jack named that one Eye Watch, because, "That horse always has one eye watching me pack him, or whatever I am doing. But he is a good husky animal for packing ore or in the harness and I try to keep away from his rear hoofs," Jack laughingly told Hattie. "I have the ranchers looking for a good, gentle saddle horse for you, Dear. Out Three Creek Ranch way or over at Mac Prunty's Ranch in Charleston, they have plenty of good well-broken horses."

It was only a week later that a cowboy rode into the yard leading a beautiful blaze-faced bay horse. Hattie was driven by a wild desire to possess that fine gelding. She wanted the feel of his warm hide against her hands, wanted to caress his neck, to speak to the horse and have him conscious of her. He turned his head so that his dark eyes could look at her with affection.

Hattie stepped over to the horse and slipped her hand under his forelock, running her hand down the gleaming white face to the soft velvet of his nose. He was sensitive of the affection given him by this warmhearted woman and showed it by the constant flickering of his sensitive ears and the pride that arched his neck.

"This horse will be aware of the joy of living and the warm sun and the cool grass," thought Hattie. "I will never let anyone be mean to him, he's beautiful, perfect!" She clucked to him and he dropped his muzzle into her palm, breathing warmly and huffed to her.

He had white markings up all four legs ending evenly as though they were stockings.

"Stockings! We will name him Stockings, maybe Socks sometimes for short," exclaimed Hattie joyfully. "Look at that long flowing mane and tail, and the tail reaches the ground. I love him, you will buy him for me, won't you, Jack dear? All for my very own?" Hattie rambled on. "He seems gentle so that Gracie can walk around him, you know how she has taken to horses, guess she will be your boy-helper one day soon. I can hardly keep track of her."

Hattie's mouth was dry with excitement. "I hear some of the ladies are forming a riding club, now I will join them and be so proud of Stockings."

When Jack could interrupt he asked the cowboy how much he owed for the horse and some other particulars he needed to know.

"This is the best saddle horse that the Clarks at Three Creek Ranch had. He is part Morgan and was broken and gentled the right way. Your wife and children will be very safe with him. He is only five years old and broke to harness also. The price is one hundred dollars to you, Jack. Mr. Clark told me to tell you that he threw in the fine saddle and bridle for the same price."

"Good, I'll make you out a check right away. Come in and have something to eat, and, look, you'd better stay overnight."

"Thanks," said the young cowhand, "I'll stop awhile then go back to Jarbidge — got a room there and a stall for my horse. Want to have a few drinks and play a little poker before I go back to the ranch tomorrow."

As he left, Hattie and Jack turned to go back into their new home. With arms around each other they were happy.

"We finished the house, barn, cellar and chicken shed just in time," Jack said, as he turned his head toward the sky and saw the dark clouds approaching.

The Commercial Club members planned a Labor Day Celebration with foot races for children, sack races, a tug-o-war for the men and even the ladies lifted their skirts to race. Of course the main event was a drilling contest. Will Martin and Mike Pavlak had drawn top honors for the drilling contest and were to compete for the one hundred dollar purse. Martin was one of the professional single and double jack drillers in the area.

A single jack was a four pound hammer used by one man and a double jack weighed twice that amount. The handle of the double jack was usually thirty-six inches long though sometimes a longer or shorter length to suit the driller.

The most difficult part of double jacking was to strike the drill hard and squarely on the drill head. This needed a steady nerve and keen eye, which Will and Bill Roland, the other half of the team, had.

"We dress our drill bits so that they are just right," Will told a bystander. "They must be tempered hard and chisel-shaped. We can tell by the feel of the hammer when a drill isn't cutting fast and has gotten dull. Then the drill holder changes bits. Roland and I are a good team, we have been in some tight places where the hammer just missed the holder's head and the drill had to be hit on an angle.

"We have entered many contests in Goldfield and Wyoming," continued Martin. "Our record for a thirty-inch hole in hard rock is twenty-five minutes."

When the double jacker tires, he changes position and he holds the drill. Therefore, the partner must be half of a perfect team, trained equally well.

Martin and Roland won the purse that day from the opposing couple.

Shortly after Labor Day, President Ray left as the club's representative for the Mining Congress in Los Angeles. To publicize the Jarbidge District he took three hundred pounds of ore samples from the claim owners.

Out on top of the mountain plateau, an early storm caught the band of sheep before they were taken to their winter range. A canvas-covered wagon stood hunched on a windy and snowy spot. Its chimney smoke streaked across the cold grey sky. A dirty mass of sheep huddled near by, blatting pitifully. The camp tender

56

walked around with his sheepskin collar turned against the wind. The two dogs at his heels waited for some word of action. With the storm getting worse and the yapping of coyotes in the distance, a desire to hunt them down rose in the camp tender. He had smelled the wind, watched the horizon and studied the birds flying and knew the blizzard was coming.

Typical Basque Sheepherders wagon

Surely the herder would be back before dark. He promised before he left for the little town of Jarbidge to get a jug of wine. He didn't have far to go.

The large main had drifted into a sheltered basin in the trees near a protecting ridge. For sheep are the most helpless of animals. Their teeth are grinders back in the upper jaw, useless for fighting. The short front teeth are only for grazing the thin grasses, or the tender but bitter sagebrush tips of the winter range. Sheep are not fast enough to run from attack nor have they the endurance to buck a storm or flooded gully. Whatever chance at life is theirs, the herder gives them. No sheep will face wind-driven snow. They drift with it, fearing and knowing they must escape. Sometimes they pile blindly into arroyos or sheltered pockets, one on top of the other, crushing and smothering one another.

The tender knew there was nothing he could do for the sheep so he climbed into the wagon. The door banged shut behind him and he was lonely. However, he thought just as soon as he had saved some money he would go back to his homeland. He was a young Basque and had come to the United States for two or three years. The Basque would make lots of money for they paid well in this country. Then he could go back to his native land and his family and marry the beautiful girl he left there.

The yapping of the coyotes sounded nearer now. If by morning three or four ewes had been cut out of the herd by a killer coyote and the half eaten carcasses were there, surely the camp mover or owner would not blame him or the herder. He might have a government trapper come out and cautiously set poison and traps to catch the coyotes.

One such trapper, Edward DeBernardi, had been employed by the United States Government for many years. His job was to trap predatory animals such as cougars, bobcats, coyotes and he had even been known to trap a bear on top of Coon Creek Mountain, just a mere ten miles from Jarbidge. The sheep men were eager to have these trappers, so they gave them food and bed in their main sheep camps.

CHAPTER 12

Jarbidge had settled down and become a better organized mining camp by Thanksgiving of 1910. Many of the early capitalists and transients had left. The week of stormy weather had cleared and the day of Thanksgiving promised to be beautiful. Since the new club building had been completed for the "First Grand Ball," the residents were grateful. To build the clubhouse, funds and days of labor were donated by miners and businessmen of the town. However, the hiring of a special carpenter to speed up the work added to the cost of the building; but the amount was only eleven hundred dollars and the club treasury, since initiating one hundred forty-five new members, was in good shape.

The log building was an attractive structure, sixty by twenty-three feet in dimension and the partly dressed logs were squared on the inside with an adz. The construction, typical of that era, had long timbers running to the high roof through the open ceiling. The maple floor, laid as a floating floor — not attached to the walls — made it one of the most unusual and finest club buildings in that part of the State of Nevada. For the Thanksgiving ball, the floor was planed, smoothed and waxed to a mirror finish. The club bought a piano and had it freighted in for the occasion, this being quite an accomplishment since it was by wagon and teams. Ladies of Jarbidge and Pavlak worked diligently for two days with the ball committee to decorate the hall.

Hattie and Jack joined in the planning and decorating. Hattie baked cakes and pies for midnight refreshments. The ball, a special affair for a rough, new mining camp, conveyed an extra touch of elegance.

The word PROGRESS worked in three foot high letters of evergreen extended across the width of the back wall. Evergreen branches decorated the hall entrance and the walls. Notices hung about the hall advising the dancers, such as: "We strive to please — ourselves," "If you don't see what you want — forget it," and others.

The evening brought out a full complement of the ladies of the camp. Hattie loved to dance so when the fiddle tuned up and the music started playing the opening waltz, she slipped into Jack's arms and glided gracefully across the dance floor. They made a lovely couple. All the roughness of a prospector-miner seemed to

58

float away and Jack danced with the smoothness which became him. This tall, slender man held his head high.

The souvenir programs for the ball were appropriate, listing a series of dances such as the Pioneer's Waltz, Jarbidge two-step, Our Club three-step, Future Prosperity polka and Old Folks quadrille.

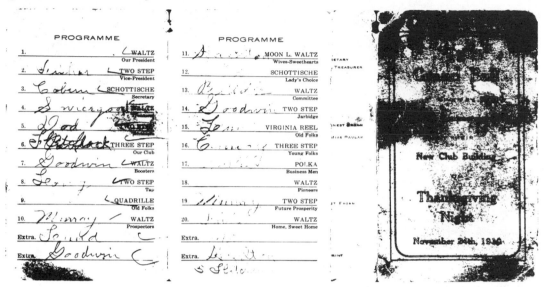

Hattie was popular and her souvenir program was filled before the evening had much more than begun. Will Martin, who hoped to marry her sister Pearl some day, enticed Hattie to let him put his name on her program for three dances.

The exquisite gowns of the ladies and the somber dark suits of the men presented an unusual scene in a supposedly crude, uncultured mining camp in the West. The costumes, dances and atmosphere might have been mistaken for a ball in any Eastern city. The couples whirled through schottisches and quadrilles. "Gents to the right, ladies to the left — now let's all join partners and Promenade," sang the caller.

The refreshments served at midnight consisted of cold turkey, boiled ham, bread, rolls, cake, pies, coffee, apples and oranges.

Ten students attended the first school in Jarbidge, the year of 1910. A small log cabin built just below the outcropping of rock across the river from the main street. The teacher was Mrs. Evans and the students were: Faye McCormick, Marion Strong, Gladys and Herb Pangborn and Priscilla, Mrs. Evans' daughter. Then there was Lesley Ward, Loren Ray, Alice Fletcher and her brothers, Owen and Wood. As Alice was only five years old she spent most of the time by the stove saying, "Isn't it time to go home — isn't it time to go home?"

The next year the Elko County School District had allocated some lots on the main street for a building and playground and when the school year started the students had a nice new school building to use. The teacher was Miss Bittermark Wolf. The following year the teacher, Miss Campbell, came all the way from Pavlak every school day.

For many days, the main street of the town had been lined with big freight wagons loaded with lumber and supplies for the cyanide plant which was being built at the Pavlak millsite. The manager of the company had been busy supervising the development work on the mine, hauling in and hewing of logs for the mill foundations and looking after this incoming freight, which included assisting the freighters over the bad road, where every day there were accidents and often the teams rolled over the grade. The road builders from Twin Falls and from Deeth were not aware of the early arrival of this large amount of freight so had not been rushing for better ways in and out of the camp with less grade percentage. An abundance of capital from Deeth and Elko County and a large force of men and teams steadily moved ahead building the road from the railroad at Deeth to Charleston and on into the forest. When they came to the grades leading to the summit they encountered too much snow and enormous drifts; therefore at Dead Horse Construction Camp the crew stopped for the winter.

The new year dawned on a white world. The pale sun did little to warm the zero temperature especially since it arrived in the canyon at ten in the morning and left by four in the afternoon. The leafless trees glittered and the green needles of the conifers were jeweled with hoarfrost. The aspens sparkled like patterns in cut glass. This beauty could not last, the dark clouds came and a storm blew in from the south. Why was it that the winds always came from the south, over Cougar Mountain? The wind howled and the snow swirled against the windows of Goodwin's log cabin in Pavlak. Snowslides tore trees and loosened tons of rock and earth in the canyon between their home and Jarbidge, leaving huge gashes on the slopes.

The driving wind penetrated the warmest clothing of man and the thickest fur of beast. From the hill above the cabin came the cry of a coyote. Soon it was joined by the voices of others. They feared the storm and knew they would be hungry before it was over — maybe it would last for days and their bellies would be empty. Heads held high to the wind and driven ice, their voices rose in a chorus of wailing crescendos and ended in little barks. Many animals deserted the high country to take up residence in sight of the cabin. The mule deer came down into the yard and

60

Hattie tossed out bread, apples or food which they ate. Jack dropped hay around for them.

Goodwin's Cabin in Winter

Families moved closer to the stoves, watched the supply of wood diminish and hoped soon a ray of sunshine would penetrate the cloudy sky. Jack had made the log cabin warm and sturdy and the big heating stove in the living room was filled with mountain mahogany, a hardwood that burned hot and lasted long. The flames licked at the isinglass window in the big stove. With the kitchen range chuck-full of hot coals the home was warm and cozy.

CHAPTER 13

Jack came home from town, and was so happy about something — Hattie realized he was about to burst with information but she did not ask him what had happened. Jack reached for his pipe and filled it with that sweet smelling tobacco from the familiar red can, struck a match and lit it.

"A telegram from Washington, D.C., from the President of the United States, came today taking Jarbidge townsite from the Humbolt National Forest. It was signed March 8, 1911. I have a copy of it, I'll read it to you." Jack continued, "Executive order eliminating Jarbidge townsite from Humbolt National Forest signed March 8. It is presumed that the area is the exact one hundred two and one-half acres which were recommended and a map which is undoubtedly on file in your office. Since this elimination has now officially been proclaimed by the President, you should give the matter the necessary publicity. The forest service, of course, will now have no further jurisdiction whatever over the area which has been eliminated. Very sincerely yours, E.A. Sherman, District Forester." Jack was exuberant as he read.

"That is really good news," Hattie said. She knew how the Commercial Club members had written letters to Senators, and the residents had been working to make the townsite a reality.

"I guess the business houses will appreciate this, especially the saloons," she choked back a giggle.

Jack took a few puffs on his pipe and agreed with her.

"Wait! I have more great news," he exclaimed a moment later. "We are going to have telephone service in Jarbidge and we can run a line up here to Pavlak and probably to the Bluster and the Pick and Shovel. It will be finished by September."

"How wonderful, I won't feel so isolated, Jack. Surely hope you put a line to the mine so I can call you too." Hattie was glad and that news had made her day complete.

"Charlie Winters spent the last few months getting subscribers and has signed-up sixty in the camp and along the route," said Jack.

The Idaho-Nevada Telephone Company made arrangements for the construction of a line from Jarbidge, Nevada, to Rogerson, Idaho, where it would make connections with the Bell line and serve Jarbidge, Three Creek, Cedar Creek and other ranches along the route.

The contract for construction was let to Richard Swanson, who already had the material on the ground, had a large crew, and was rushing to start work at once. The financial support from the subscribers more than covered the expenses of construction. This proved to be a valuable financial and industrial step forward for Jarbidge and Pavlak, and the company offered reasonable rates for long distance connections.

Jack seemed very enthused, and he left the house saying something about going to feed the horses.

Hattie smiled and started humming one of her favorite tunes, one which had been played at the ball last Saturday night. She thought how lovely and successful the event had been for the purpose of raising money to furnish the new schoolhouse. She was proud that it was all done by the ladies of Jarbidge and Pavlak. With a few private donations and the profit made above expenses, they could buy desks and all the furniture needed.

Then she recalled the gorgeous gowns and jewelry the ladies wore and she hoped they liked her creation. The Elko paper had printed an article about the affair, "Where is that paper?" Hattie whispered. After finding it, she scanned the article and read aloud the names and description of some of the gowns worn. "Mrs. Mike Pavlak had an olive green velvet with fur and a diamond tiara and sunburst; Mrs. John Swicegood, smoke princess trimmed with jet; Mrs. J.D. Goodwin, exquisite longeme dress made of French batiste." She thought, what a wonderful chance she had to show off her new gown. It was really a dream, and to think she had made it. The material cost so much, she felt a little guilty. The only place she knew that carried the material was George Peck's in Kansas City, but she had to have that French batiste and that certain pattern. And it was hand-embroidered around the neck and the skirt hemline.

"Well," said Hattie to herself, "the ladies surely had looked lovely," and she read on "Mrs. A.J. Lund, pale blue crepe with baby lace; Mrs. R.S. Silver, navy blue taffeta princess and point lace; Mrs. W.A. Fritz wore a gown of grey broadcloth and fur and her daughter Mona, a very dainty and hand embroidered Irish linen." Oh, yes! she remembered the gorgeous gown Mrs. Ben Hazelton wore which was old rose French silk methaline trimmed in all-over spangled net and brilliants. Hattie didn't finish the list of names but picked up her guitar, strummed and sang "Down By The Old Mill Stream."

"What a blessing," Hattie said, happily to Jack after he returned to the house. "They have set two days aside this summer for work on a good road to Jarbidge and will have foot bridges across the streams and gulches. Hope they put handrails on the bridges. We have to plan for the future when Gracie will be walking those two long miles to school. Of course she can walk with the Seine girls and Mable, then young Bert and Roy Yewell will be going soon too. I hope that trudging through the deep snow doesn't hurt our two little girls."

"It will make good strong women of them," said Jack.

"Well, if it doesn't kill them before they become grown into womanhood. Snow slides have been real bad this past winter and I haven't been sleeping well nights thinking about them." Hattie's unhappiness and worry were evident.

Jack, his crew of men and the teams, had about finished the road leading out of the canyon at Pavlak, up the mountainside to the crest. Then it switched back continuing around the other side. This section was difficult to survey; it was steep and the cost to build was great. The route then went to Bear Creek Meadows and to Bear Creek Summit of 8,488 feet elevation, cut into the mountainside and on to Coon Creek Summit; then to Dead Horse Camp where the other crew, coming from Charleston, had stopped last fall because of the heavy snowstorms. The camp where the crew lost a horse when it got down frantically fighting in a snowbank and smothered to death. The men cut the team loose and saved the other horse.

Jarbidge to Charleston Road viewed from Bluster Mine

In surveying and building the road, Jack encountered steep grades, dangerous curves, springs and many obstacles. Men and horses worked hard and Jack had been coming home so tired every night that he told Hattie he hoped his strength would hold out to finish the project as he had promised the Commercial Club members he would. The Club knew that Jack was their man because he had the determination and the skill. He worked his horses, but never abused them because he realized what dependence was put upon the animals. But his men and horses were about done in.

"I know we need that route out of this end of the canyon," Jack told Hattie. "It takes us to our Elko County seat, also to Deeth, on the railroad, whose residents and businessmen have done much for us and our freight business. Although I know the road will never stay open in the winters unless a crew is kept to open the snowbanks. Just can't figure a way out around those snowslides." Jack talked on as though he was trying to determine another route since he knew that mountain well. "Can't go down into Coon Creek Canyon and then pull up out, too steep, still have to cross Coon Creek Summit; it is the best I can do.

"Some year, in the future, they might survey a road which could be open all year, but I doubt it. In the summer and fall people will enjoy the scenery, the meadow

64

Danger Point

and the flowers. Hattie, you should see all the flowers starting to bloom, yellow sunflowers, blue lupine and chokecherry bushes. By fourth of July they will cover the hillsides with their color. You just go out of a forest of pine trees and come into young quakies, then see the hillsides of flowers." Hattie was proud that Jack noticed the scenery and flowers.

When the planned road came into the large pine trees, the work involved sawing a path through and snaking the logs out of the way with horses. Boulders had to be blasted and removed which meant hand drilling the holes for the dynamite. Jack hired Will Martin and his partner who were excellent drillers. There seemed to be no possible way out of the canyon Southwest to Charleston except upgrade, a climb of nearly fourteen percent in one place, then on to Bear Creek and Coon Creek Summits. Between the summits the mountain slope extended to thousands of feet from the top to the canyon floor, and in places was heavily wooded. Danger and Windy Points lay on this slope between the two summits and always had many slides during the winters and early springs and Jack could find no way around that area.

Nevertheless, by the end of July, 1911, the new wagon road from Jarbidge, down into the ranch country of Charleston and on to Deeth was completed and the engineering over the steep grades, through pine forests and aspen groves was well done.*

Two days in July were set apart to build a good road from Jarbidge to Pavlak. This would connect with the Pavlak to Charleston and Deeth road just completed by Jack and his crew. Those two days saw a large and spontaneous turnout of willing volunteers. Professional men, businessmen, in fact all those in the camps, with many who were working prospects, came out early with their picks, shovels and axes. They built bridges and crossed the river only twice. The ladies of the camps supplied lunches for the workers as their share in the new road, while the Commercial Club supplied plenty of beer.

Hattie said, "Pavlak and Jarbidge people never do things by halves and they can be depended upon to meet any move made by their neighbors."

This road is used today and has never been changed. It is still as beautiful with flowers and pines and stands of quakies which change colors with the coming of fall seasons. The points still have their snowslides. Because of them the road is not open until the last of June for automobile travel when it is opened by County crews with dynamite and mechnical equipment.

65

CHAPTER 14

With no pride of ancestry nor hope of posterity, the mule must somewhere have statues erected in his honor.

Patrick Donohue, native of Ireland, came to Jarbidge with his five large mules. He came for supplies to do some prospecting across the mountains in the rough crater range. He had found rich gold color on a remote creek in that rugged crater area, east of Jarbidge. He staked two claims and had taken precautions to keep the find a secret until he could get some supplies of dynamite, tools and food for a month's stay, then he intended staking some more discoveries if these proved as good as he thought.

His mules were magnificent animals. They could carry heavy loads at a steady pace, up and down mountains, and across rough terrain. They could forage for themselves better than horses.

Pat was not a drinking man, but he stopped in the Mint Bar for an opportunity to be friendly and to observe reports of other prospectors and miners.

"Pat, you are a sight fur sore eyes," shouted Nick Vucovitch, a Czechoslovakian who hit every boom town. "I ain't seen you since Couer d'Alene days."

Donohue waved a hand in recognition. "Likely you're right there, Nick, didn't expect to see you here in Jarbidge." Pat was somewhat uneasy but he had worked with Nick and thought maybe he could trust him. They started talking and slipped over to an unused poker table and sat down. Pat told Nick about his find and locations in the craters and that he had his mules packed for the trip back.

"Do you think dat's a secret? Eh, Pat? I was over dere last week, and found me, Nick, in de middle of a dozen udder prospectors wid packs. I tell myself, I better go home. . . You can trust me, Patrick, I like mighty well to hear wut ya got over dere." The Czech started showing some enthusiasm, that was his favorite area. "I know dis Jarbidge ledge runs over dere into do craters. When'er you headin' back?"

"I aim to start before daylight, do you want to go with me, Nick? I'm riding the only horse I got, the mules are all packed. Do you have a horse to ride?"

"Yah, Pat, thanks fur askin' me. Why don't you bunk wid me tonight? I got a cabin up de street and we'd get an early start? Better — it's snowing a little and when de camp's asleep we will leave. I got my horse put up in de barn."

Pat did not protest. That was to his liking. They awakened at four in the morning and within the hour they had taken to the trail. Each mule found its usual place in line. Not a light was visible in the camp as they crossed over the trail pass. They paused momentarily to look at the stars.

"Did ya ever see anyt'ing prettier?" Vucovitch said in a low voice. "Like a kid wid a fourt' of July sparkler."

A man had no age when tomorrow showed a fresh show of color in the pan. Nick was seldom discouraged — the next day always held promise, and while he had never made a rich strike, what gold ore he had managed to mine seemed to provide him with the necessities and bolster his ambitions.

The new snow muffled their sounds and would cover the sign of their exit. By morning there would be no trace to excite suspicion.

Daylight was slow in coming and it had brought a let-up in the snow storm. The mules showed no indication of fatigue, though the men were tired. Nick and Pat stopped to cook and eat before they went on over the saddle which led into the craters.

Pat's mules recognized a master and tried no foolishness with him. They were trained to follow one another on a trail and even to follow a bell mare when turned out at night. The sure-footed animals plodded along, big ears flapping, indifferent to discomforts. The trail was not only upward and rough but to the side, like a carelessly balanced dish. One mule in the center of the string, slipped and was forced to scramble. The pitching around shifted the packsaddle until it was underneath the animal. This added to the difficulties and overbalanced the mule until it was off the trail and slipping down the steep slope below. Finally the animal came to a stop, still on its feet, much less disconcerted than a horse would have been in such a predicament.

Pat waited until he was sure the other animals would not panic and then he looked over the situation. The steep slippery slope between the mule and the trail made an impossible climb. He would have to go down there and then, after shifting the pack into position and securing it, lead the mule to a spot where, by attaching a rope to the mule and he and Nick pulling from above, it could be helped and hoisted to the trail. And this was done successfully.

Then they threaded their way along the very narrow, shale covered trail that led over the crest of the crater and down the other slope which brought them to the claims. The mules were laden with dynamite, a wheelbarrow, pickaxes, shovels, bedding and some food including beans, flour, coffee and bacon; and some oats for the mules and saddle horses.

It was late in the afternoon when the two men and pack train arrived at the spot where Pat had left his discovery point. They unpacked the mules and made a fine camp in the protection of a stand of pine trees. Just out in the clearing they built a fire, warmed themselves and cooked some supper. Tomorrow they could kill a deer and have venison. They could eat a small buck or doe while they were camped there. The meadow within sight was where the mules would eat and stay close. Pat knew his trustworthy animals and took care of them. He fed them a little oats everyday, so they came for their extra goodies.

The moon shone bright and full that night. The deer came into the meadow to feed with the mules. It was cold and clear, but the two men kept warm and talked about their prospecting and the gold to be found. They would build a small arrastra to do some crude milling.

After two weeks Pat and Nick arrived back in Jarbidge to record their claims and brought some good samples of ore. This excited the men of the camp about the crater district and some left for there at once.

Freighting into Jarbidge

"Dick, Duke, damn you, get up!" shouted Slim after he climbed over the front wheel to his seat, gathered in the slack of the jerk line and loosened the wagon brake. "Git up, and don't let me down. We have material for the Bourne Mill on this outfit and have to be in Jarbidge within three days." Slim Walsh had a way of talking to his horses, he cursed them and made them pull heavy loads, but he fed them well and cared for them as if they were his children.

He had two wagons heavily loaded with the mill and machinery, and an eight-horse team to pull it. Dick and Duke, the lead team, were the smallest horses, alert, quick to learn and follow a command. Next in line were the swing team, then the pointers and the wheelers. The pointers, hitched to the end of the tongue, were helpful to the wheelers which were the heaviest team, and the most dependable pullers. They were the ones Slim depended upon to keep from getting stuck in the mud. They knew how to get down close to the ground so as to deliver more power, and when Slim yelled, "Now, Blue — Shortie, do your stuff!" they really pulled.

In rounding a sharp turn or dodging a badger hole Slim would tighten the reins of the pointers and they soon learned what that meant. The lead horses would have to be put off the road to keep the rear wagon from running off the road on the other side. If that side happened to be a rock cliff and a steep-slope, like the Crippen Grade, results would be disastrous. A sharp hairpin turn with a long team required clever work by both Slim and the team.

Each freight outfit had a set of bells. Slim's were clear and loud and fastened to the lead team. There were eight bells fastened on the hames and their main purpose was to alert an approaching teamster. Backing a freight wagon and team was almost impossible. A good teamster would stop and walk ahead, look around a curve or down a steep, long hill before he proceeded.

Another purpose of the bells was to alert the other horses. The lead team moved first, causing the traces to tighten and the bells to ring. Slim was one of the best freighters in the country and when he shouted "Hiya — Hiya!" and called the horses' names in order, they tightened up their tugs and the wheels slowly started to turn. They leaned into their collars, cautiously at first, keeping a strong steady pull, and as the wheels rolled faster the horses moved faster. They had a heavy load to pull.

Slim hired a swamper to help him brush and curry the horses and do many odd jobs. But he usually did his own horseshoeing. Freight horses had to be kept shod. Sometimes a horse in the rear would step on the projecting heel of the shoe of the one in front, and wrench the shoe off. Or the shoe would catch on a piece of rock.

The incoming freight to Jarbidge included everything from ore crushers, lumber, big cooking ranges, barrels of whiskey and kegs of beer, to Faye McCormack's square grand piano. The piano was the one on which Grace Goodwin took lessons from Faye, lovely daughter of the mercantile store owner. Gracie did look forward to those lessons, she loved music, even asked, "Mamma, will you buy me a piano?"

CHAPTER 15

Jarbidge had a school, post office, clubhouse and many business establishments, but no church. Hattie Goodwin, Mrs. Baker and other ladies were concerned about the moral tone of the community, especially about the children, who needed a Sunday School. Easter of 1912 was approaching and the group asked Hattie if she could find and communicate with a traveling minister who would come into Jarbidge for part of the Easter week.

She had heard about Reverend Howell in Elko and wrote to him. He answered promptly, accepting the invitation; he would hold religious services and have Bible readings. When Hattie told the ladies the good news, they were pleased and started cleaning the clubhouse, planning for a blessed Easter week. This would be the first sermon ever preached in Jarbidge and was quite an undertaking, besides it would be interesting to watch the outcome. Hattie hoped this would not be the last sermon in Jarbidge.

The residents welcomed Reverend Howell. Men and women of all classes were courteous and hospitable. He and his party were given lodging, food and a key to the Commercial Club Hall, and members were eager to make his stay comfortable.

In their endeavor to furnish the hall well, the club had recently bought four large solid oak rocking chairs and two long settees, all with leather seats, also many wooden folding chairs.

Of course there was the huge iron heating stove and always plenty of wood to keep a crackling hot fire.

Ladies with their husbands and children walked two miles from Pavlak to the services, and Jarbidge people were happy to attend. Saloons closed their doors for Easter day and night. The town took on a different mood and attitude. For the five days and evenings the audience ran from forty-two to seventy-six. Nine men sang with the choir Easter night. They had solos and quartettes and the talent was unusually good.

The congregation sang hymns, the minister led them in prayer, and then with a quiet beyond apprehension, he read the story of the Crucifixion according to the Gospel of St. Luke.

The Goodwin family sat near the front and Jack tried very hard to listen and be attentive.

70

Reverend Howell read: " 'And he took bread, and gave thanks, and brake it, and gave unto them, saying, This is my body which is given for you: this do in remembrance of me.' "

Yes, thought Jack, reading himself a lecture, I should be more considerate of my wife and children and — of my friends.

" 'And truly the Son of man goeth, as it was determined: but woe unto that man by whom he is betrayed!' "

Were there men in that building who felt as damned as Judas? Jack knew there to be good men, husbands and fathers who were lusting after the flesh. He would try to not name those men in his mind but he thought on — deliberately — and even he was not perfect; he had found such thoughts pleasurable. He had wanted to hold that young one in his arms and kiss her — that night he met her at the dance. He was shocked at himself. With effort he turned his attention to St. Luke.

" 'And there followed him a great company of people, and of women, which also bewailed and lamented him.

" 'But Jesus turning unto them said, Daughters of Jerusalem, weep not for me, but weep for yourselves, and for your children.' "

On Jack's right side sat Hattie, erect and attentive and next to her his younger daughter, so much like Hattie. On his left hand sat Gracie, his elder. Was she his likeness, his favorite?

The minister read to the end of the chapter and led the congregation in prayer. The service was over.

Jarbidge Commercial Clubhouse after Modern Restoration

The camp's exposure to and interest shown in a preacher and the Bible readings was remarkable. Hattie told Reverend Howell how badly the town needed a Sunday School. He agreed to arrange that she be sent weekly Sunday School lessons, pamphlets and hymnal books. She promised to walk or ride horseback and bring her two children to the schoolhouse every Sunday morning and give the town children an hour of Bible study and singing and they would study the lessons he sent.

During the week the minister and his party were in Jarbidge, there was a fresh fall of snow which made the summits and passes over the mountains to Charleston and Elko difficult and dangerous. District Attorney Disart was in Jarbidge so he accompanied Reverend Howell and party on the outgoing trip. The first day they attempted to go from town but were five hours making Coon Creek Summit, a distance of ten miles, only to be forced back to camp because of the raging storm and the huge snowdrifts.

"The next day the storm had abated," wrote the Reverend in his letter of thanks to Hattie and the committee, "but the traveling was even worse. As we were accompanying the mail stage which left at the unreasonable hour of noon, we were forced into night travel. At ten o'clock we found the fresh fallen snow had so covered the old trail that it was impossible to follow it in the dark. We then camped on the trail keeping ourselves warm by campfire and foraging for wood until daylight permitted us to proceed."

A stage was added to the back of the clubhouse building and a storm door and flagpole erected on the front. The women were given one night a week for card parties, box lunches, minstrel shows and other events. Through these benefits the women obtained enough money to have a stage curtain made which was attached to a wooden roller across the stage front and by a pulley rope ran from the ceiling to the floor and back again. The heavy muslin curtain had a Venetian scene painted in the center and local merchants' advertisements bordered the picture.*

The sanitary committee of the club demanded that the camp be cleaned up at once and kept clean. All refuse, manure, cans, bottles and garbage appearing on a person's premise or on a vacant lot within the town limits must be removed to the dump grounds down the canyon. Residents were instructed to dig deep holes for privies and disinfect them from time to time with lime or wood ashes. With these warnings, the sanitary committee hoped to eliminate flies and therefore keep down diseases, and those who did not heed the requests were prosecuted.

This stage curtain has been repaired by Mrs. Thelma Calhoun and the Nevada Historical Society, Carson City, Nevada. In 1974, the curtain will be displayed at the Jarbidge Commercial Club Building.

CHAPTER 16

Hattie's and Jack's friendship with William Martin went back to the days when they were all in Encampment, Wyoming. It was there he met Pearl, Hattie's youngest sister. Will thought about Pearl a lot and knew with just half a chance he could love her. Of course Pearl had her sights toward drama and traveling.

Will was a charter member of the Jarbidge Commercial Club, a Pavlak resident and had a good job at the Pick and Shovel Mine. Also, with his prospecting and locating claims in the new gold district, he knew he had a wonderful chance of making some real money.

About time I got married, Will thought, I have been a bachelor long enough. In all my travels I have never found a sweet, little, bright-eyed girl like Pearl. So I must think up some proposition and ask Hattie if we can get her to come to Jarbidge.

He talked to Hattie about Pearl, where she was and what she was doing.

"Would she come to visit you, Hattie, if you asked her? Will you listen to a plan I have to get her here? Then leave the rest to me?" Will pleaded.

"What is your plan? Remember I love my little sister. She has always come to me when I needed her." Hattie spoke sincerely. "When Helen was born in Kansas, Pearl administered the chloroform because the nurse could not get to our house the same time Dr. Seright did. Then when I was so ill in Goldfield, she came when I wrote for her. Jack was out on a prospecting trip and I couldn't reach him. I had a miscarriage and the doctor in Goldfield thought it was caused by chopping wood, the board sprung back and gave me quite a jolt.

"Anyway, Pearlie was only nineteen but she nursed me back to health until we got word to Jack and he came. Then she found work in the booming gold camp. Nevertheless, I will listen, since you are a good friend." Hattie registered a little more enthusiasm.

"I want to marry Pearl," said Will. "Want to very badly. Have never met another girl like that pretty little spit-fire. I will give you enough money for a one-way trip and you send it to her. One way, mind you, not a round trip. Have her stay a month with you folks and leave the rest to me. I will persuade her to marry me. I love her and I will court her as she has never been cherished before." His voice became more eager with every word he spoke.

"If she will marry me I'll build her a house, a cabin here in Pavlak. Buy her a horse and give her whatever she wants, but most of all, I'll give her my true devotion. I'm sincere, Hattie."

"I really believe you are, Will, although you are — maybe ten years older than Pearl, you just might be good for her. She must settle down soon. Anyway, I'll think it over. Give you an answer next time you come to the house."

Will could hardly wait for the answer. He went to work with a light heart. Whenever he had a spare day he prospected in the Bourne Gulch, he knew where he could find good ore. He would show that little beauty he could make a fortune for her.

Only a few days passed before Will visited the Goodwin cabin. Hattie had told Jack about the plan and he thought — for Pearl, it was the best thing he had heard.

"She needs to settle down," said Jack. "She will get herself in trouble running around the country like she does."

"I received a letter from Pearl lately, and she is in Oklahoma," assured Hattie. "I will send her the money and write for her to come visit us. But don't forget your promises, Will."

So when Pearl arrived in Jarbidge on the stage just before Thanksgiving of 1912, Hattie, Jack and Will were there to meet her. The sisters were so happy to be together again. They hugged and Hattie wondered how Pearl had taken the arduous trip in. Jack gave her a little squeeze and said, "Pearl, you remember Will Martin?"

Just then Will stepped forward, thumbed back his hat and said, "You've gotten prettier since I saw you last, Pearl." He could feel a rising sense of excitement and warmth.

She smilingly remembered the dates they had in Wyoming. "How many girls do you tell that?"

"None who'd give it more truth," he said.

She laughed timidly and her thoughts were, if ever a man was made for this rugged country, he is the one.

Pearl loved to be with Hattie and the two little girls that she knew from their birth in Kansas City. She slept in a small bed which Hattie put in the living room for her. Her life was exciting, still it was becoming relaxed and beautiful. She also began to love Will, looked forward to his visits and depended on him.

Will had done everything he told Hattie he would do. He was building a small log home in Pavlak, near Bonanza Creek. He wanted Pearl to be near her sister. He bought two spirited horses. Pearl rode the black and named him 'Ringer' and Will called his roan horse 'Indian.'

This slow-moving, slow-talking man seemed to generate an air of competence and dependability and that was really what Pearl was looking for. Yet, though his bulky frame towered over her short, dainty body, he was gentle and loving. He helped her in and out of the buggy, or on the horse. One hardly expected such manners from a Westerner and a miner. He hitched a horse to the sleigh and they took moonlight rides over the sparkling snow and into the pines. On the holidays they went with the Goodwin family to Jarbidge to dance in the Commercial Clubhouse, or attend the Christmas school play and decorated tree program.

74

Martin Cabin

Will and Pearl Martin had supper together at Gertie McCollar's. Gertie's had become an institution in Nevada, much like Delmonico's at Dodge in Midwest.

Pearl was silent, pensive, her hands folded on the table. He sat looking at her and covered her small hands with his large, rough ones that were so professional with a single or double jack hammer. He remembered the evening she stepped out of the stage coach two months before. It seemed two days. Yet, in that short time a beautiful love had developed between them and they had gone to Twin Falls, Idaho, and been married. She was his wife and never a more exciting, lovable person had he known. He was so happy. Her eyes sparkled. She looked as though she were acting in a play at the time.

Sounds of shots and wild miner yells split the evening quiet. He stood up and wrapped her coat around her.

"This is payday and guess the miners are loaded," he announced. "Maybe I'd better get you to the hotel room. I have a little business to take care of and then I will be right there."

75

"Whatever you say, Will dear," she answered.

Will led the way outside. The street was boiling with thirsty, excitement-seeking men. The newlyweds walked side by side down the wooden walk and a group of horsemen loped by. One of the horses bounded up on the duckboards.

"Keep your horse in the street," Will said.

The man pulled back on the reins, raising the horse on its haunches. "Who's tellin' me?" he yelled.

The others wheeled and circled back. One of them muttered, "It's the big guy, Martin. Better come on."

"To hell." The man slipped from the saddle. "Ain't nobody tellin' me where to ride."

Will saw the man's bearded face twist out of shape and his eyes full of hatred. He saw the man's hand curl around the butt of his pistol. Will was fast, he jumped ahead and hit the man a crashing blow on the jaw and head with his fist. The man crumpled on the boardwalk and didn't get up.

"Take him with you," Martin said curtly. "He is too drunk to be on the street."

Some of the men dismounted and gathered around their fallen companion. They muttered something as they dragged him inside the Bear Creek Saloon.

Will looked at Pearl. "I'm sorry," he said. "We will go to our home tomorrow, my Sweetheart, and forget about this."

She moved to his side and took his arm. She felt the violence fade from him. It was another part of his character that she liked. He was strong and decisive, yet he was capable of gentleness and she'd seen his compassion for his horse one day, too.

After Will saw Pearl safely to the hotel room, he went to the Recorder's Office. Recorder Rummel was still working.

"Congratulations, Martin, heard you just got back from your wedding to that pretty lady." Rummel shook hands and asked what he could do for Will.

"I want to record a claim, and thanks for the good wishes," said Will. "Yes, I am a lucky man. Have a lovely wife and a bit of good luck finding some high grade ore up Bourne Gulch. My brother Charlie will be in Jarbidge in a few days and he, Bill Roland and I are going to work my new location. Of course I have done real well on the Pick and Shovel and will not quit there for a while. So I will just record the claim, believe I will name it 'Starlight' Lode Claim. It is on the upper north side of Bourne Gulch."

With the business finished, Martin and Rummel bid each other goodnight and he went along the street to the newest hotel in town where his bride was waiting. Gertie's Nevada Hotel was the only three story building in Jarbidge. It was made of finished lumber and not logs.

On the way, Will stopped in Brauning's candy store and bought a box of chocolates. He would surprise Pearl. Benoit, the druggist, was in his place of businesss when Will passed by and he came to the open door.

"Wish you a lifetime of happiness, Martin," said Benoit.

"Thanks! I'll have it." Will was sure of that. He looked at the heavens and saw the full moon and could even find the big dipper. He thought, what a romantic night.

76

The morning dawned with fluffy white clouds in the sky. Gradually the sun lifted over the mountaintop into the canyon with a promise of a clear day. A crisp January day, but beautiful. The snow storm of three weeks ago had left the peaks and craters glistening white, but the canyon snow had melted and left only patches in the shadows.

Will arose as the sun streamed in the front window of their room. His bride awakened and he kissed her soft, warm lips.

"I'll go to the barn and get our horses saddled and bridled," Will said, as he brushed her soft brown hair from her face. "We can have breakfast and I'll find someone who has a wagon coming up our way to bring the suitcases. How is that, my Sweetheart?"

"Fine, Will dear, I'll be ready when you return."

Two hours later Pearl swung up into the saddle, watched her husband mount and they turned their horses toward Pavlak.

CHAPTER 17

Hattie and Jack sat on the porch swing in the early evening. The children were asleep. A mule buck deer came out of the thicket and walked past them. The hour was his feeding time. They saw his antlers were still in the velvet, soft and spongy looking, filled with blood for the growing of the antlers which he later might have to use in fight for supremacy. These velvet covered horns had grown from mere knobs in the early summer after he had lost his yearly rack.

Soon another buck sauntered down from the hillside, across the open yard to the river, coming for his daily supply of water. He was a younger buck and had smaller velvet antlers. It was obvious how they stayed out of the willows as a small wound would cause an imperfection in the matured bone. They were so proud.

"What beauties! Their legs look so delicate, yet they bound over brush and rocks fast and agile," whispered Hattie. "I always marvel over the softness of that velvet on the antlers." She watched the deer as they browsed. Her thoughts went back to Kansas City and compared the busy, noisy street she had left with this natural setting of beauty, the wild animals and birds and realized what the city people were missing.

"Jack, look how fat those bucks are now."

"Like all wild animals, they have built up layers of fat against the long winter when feed is scarce," Jack said. "Soon the bucks will be rubbing that velvet from their antlers. Usually they are very careful in the woods, but I remember a pitiful sight one time.

"A five-point buck got his antlers wedged between some large willows as he was trying to remove the cracked, peeling velvet. I could see where he had broken small limbs and struggled desperately, but he could not get out. Some heavy forked limbs would not release the poor animal. He evidently starved and the predators, bobcat, or cougar, had eaten half of the carcass."

Hattie sighed. "I'm glad I didn't see that."

Fall had come. There was a crispness in the air that meant white frosts would soon be upon the land. The chokecherry leaves were aflame, bright red shading into dark wine. The cottonwoods and willows along the streams were brilliant yellow.

78

Now and then a grove of aspen displayed an arrow of golden fire among the paler yellow. The patches of yellow, orange and red made a spearhead amid the solid green of the pine and cedar forest. It would not last long as the leaves would flutter to the ground, curl and brown.

Indian summer warmed the hidden trails and meadow. Hattie liked the short outings. She loitered in the woods with her two little girls, watching the squirrels and small animals at play. Often she took her .22 rifle and brought in grouse for dinner. At a range of forty yards Hattie was accurate.

Their course took them past the beaver dams, where they stopped to watch the beavers preparing their homes for the coming winter. The beaver colony paid no attention to the little family of humans, but kept dragging aspen logs and limbs down the worn path to the river. Jack had said that by watching the activities of the beavers you could tell if there was going to be a hard winter — and they were frantically working, thought Hattie.

"Let's sit on this large log and watch," said Hattie softly. "That older beaver must be the papa. He seems to be helping the younger ones roll the logs into place. Look, children, see how the beavers build their homes? They bring mud from the shallow end of the pond. They use their broad, flat tail to carry the mud and to pat it firmly between and on the logs and twigs."

Gracie suddenly moved closer to Hattie and whispered. "Mamma, look at that pretty cat looking down from the big rock above."

Hattie turned slightly to see a bob-cat watching the big beaver pull on an unusually stubborn log which had lodged on a boulder. The cat's belly bulged, evidence that he had recently eaten. "He is just curious and not eager to tangle with the strong teeth of a beaver." The cat walked on up the riverside.

Then the rest of the beaver family helped dislodge the log by pulling on one end around the rock. It moved and rolled down the slide to the stream with them running after it.

Hattie had seen an abandoned beaver home while she was in Wyoming and wanted to explain it to the children, hoping they were not too young to understand. "The beaver build a tunnel under the water, with just the right pitch so that the water flows through it but never runs swiftly enough to break it apart.

"I saw a beaver swimming in the river just below our house. We can go out evenings and watch them build their lodge or home." Hattie continued to tell about the busy little animals while Grace asked questions and listened to the story. The younger daughter watched for the beaver to come out of the water and go up the side of the bank to bring down another branch.

"After they have made their dam across the stream," said Hattie, "and the pond is deep enough so they can escape from their enemies, also can store the food pile in the bottom, then they start building a home. You see, girls, the only tools they use are their feet, teeth and tail. Their four long, orange-colored teeth, two above and two below, cut the trees down and trim off the branches and bark. And the front feet are like hands with long, strong claws which not only pat the mud, but clean and comb their fur after their frequent baths."

Hattie and the children watched while the beavers intertwined the branches and poked sticks in among the branches then added and patted the mud to fill in the holes and hold it all together.

"The walls of their homes are two feet thick of mud and sticks and they even plaster the inside so it will be smooth for the babies." Hattie was hoping they understood, and as they seemed to, she continued. "The home floor slopes toward the water plunge so the water from their wet coats will drain. Around the walls the floor is higher, making a ledge where they will sleep. Their bed is made of sweet-smelling aspen chips. You see, the babies are born in the spring and have soft fluffy fur, but the paddle-like tail is hairless and their eyes open the day they are born. The beavers dive to the bottom of the pond and enter a secret doorway that leads to a hole in the floor of their home.

"When the first frost comes they have stored their food away, the dam is strong and their home is snug and solid; Mr. and Mrs. Beaver are ready for their first winter together. The roof extends out of the water and after it freezes it becomes as hard as a steel shell, so they sleep soundly.

"The Diamond A Ranch owners like beaver dams in Buck Creek so the water does not flow fast taking the soil with it, then they often irrigate a little hay meadow during the summer with a beaver pond run-off."

Hattie realized it was getting late and the sun was setting towards the mountains, so she said, "Girls, we must go home now."

"Can we come back tomorrow, Mamma?" The girls hated to leave and miss seeing the beavers again.

"We will see," said Hattie, "maybe we can watch the beaver family near our house."

On their way home a weasel darted into a ground squirrel's burrow. Had he seen the squirrel before he entered the burrow? The weasel, mink and marten kill even when they aren't hungry, their killing is wanton. Somewhere Hattie had read that; how sad. Not like the bobcat that could look with curiosity upon the beavers when his belly was full.

Would she like to trap animals? Hattie thought she might ask Jack about it, maybe not this winter, but next. She had learned much about the West and its wild inhabitants. They interested her. She would send for some literature and books about the animals and how to trap them legally.

80

CHAPTER 18

The telephone line began operating between Jarbidge and Twin Falls. Since the camp was comparatively new and so isolated from outside communications, residents rejoiced over the progress which had been made. A day later, the line in use from Jarbidge to Pavlak and extending to the Bluster and Pick and Shovel Mines made many people happy, even though they had three-party lines.

Hattie's ring was one, Pearl's two rings and Pick and Shovel had three rings. Even though Pearl lived a very short distance from Hattie, she called her often on the phone by ringing one ring and not going through the Jarbidge operator.

One day Pearl heard the three rings and wanted to eavesdrop on the conversation, eager to hear who was calling the Pick and Shovel Mine since her husband worked there.

After quietly lifting the receiver she heard . . .

"Hello! Big Swede, this is Alice."

"Alice Who!" shouted the voice on the mine phone. Swede had to shout over the interference of the newly installed telephone line and the noise of men talking in the bunkhouse.

"Madam Alice, you know me, Swede. Why haven't you been down to see me lately? Been over two weeks."

"OH—Alice Baby. I've been workin' overtime, been powerful busy. Gettin' ready to ship some bullion. But, I'll be down to see you soon."

"O.K., I guess it's just as well, because I haven't felt so good and my back has sure been bothering me lately."

"Back, you said, Alice? You been feelin' bad? Well — never you mind, I'll be down this week-end and take care of you."

Click! went the party line, Pearl could hardly contain herself until she hung the receiver up on the hook at the side of the new oak phone. Her imagination was running away and she exploded with laughter and when she knew Big Swede and Alice were off the line, she rang one ring to tell Hattie the best joke she had heard in all her eavesdropping.

The Jarbidge jail was completed and ready for use. Made of cement, it had two cells and a small front room.

Clark and Fletcher had constructed a ten-stamp mill on the North Star property and were financially backed. This mine had over twelve hundred feet of tunnels and was one of the most extensively developed in the camp.

Staley's saw mill, in operation seven miles up the Jarbidge River, had access to pine, balsam and cottonwood trees. It was the largest in the district. One of the young Staley sons met a tragic death when he accidently got in the way of the big motor-driven round blade.

Staley's Sawmill

There were portable saw mills in and around Bear Creek Meadows, Coon Creek Summit and behind the town of Jarbidge on the mountainside. The town was fortunate to be situated in a forest that could furnish the lumber for mine timbers, props, mills and business establishments, also for residents.

Mr. and Mrs. Fritz built a bottlehouse and operated it as a restaurant; George Strobel, furniture; Griffin and Curoe ran the Northern Hotel and Cafe and later Curoe opened a saloon in Pavlak. A grocery store was open for business and Benoit owned and operated the drug store. The town had a physician, C.E. Colby, a dentist, D.J. Gilliland and Roy R. Cook the attorney.

Mr. J.S. (John) Berry's General Merchandise store stocked such items as Levis, carbide lamps and lanterns, Mackinaws, long underwear, ladies' and men's and children's button shoes, soap, hairbrushes and boot laces. Also cosmetics, jewelry, corsets, stationery, kerosene lamps, coffee ground in the store and stacks of gloves. All this and much more was jammed into that small store. The merchant always seemed to be able to find what anyone asked for.

"Yes!" Mr. Berry said in his familiar slow drawl. "I have what you want and believe I know right where it is." He never hurried and some uncanny instinct guided him straight to the desired object from the shelves of boxed merchandise or the high piled counters. He might have to dive into one of those chaotic piles or choose from cooking utensils or stove supplies which were heaped on the floor, but with a smile of triumph and a whistled tune only familiar to Mr. Berry, he would come up with the wanted article.

Jarbidge had been given a great deal of publicity during the last two years on account of the wonderful gold and silver showing. Travel into and out of the camp increased. Freight was hauled on wagons from the railroad at Deeth to Charleston, a distance of fifty-two miles. When weather permitted supplies and mining equipment was freighted into Jarbidge from the Deeth Mercantile Store.

As the winter months approached, the teamsters carried both wheels and runners on the loads. Where they encountered a bare spot on the road, where the wind had blown the snow away, wheels were used. But where the snow was deep and sleighing was good, the drivers changed to the runners and the heavy wagon trains proceeded.

The passenger and mail stage ran three times a week. There were two feed stations between Deeth and Charleston. The stage which had headquartered in Jarbidge with an established feed station at Dead Horse Camp, met the Deeth stage at Charleston. It took six hours to go from Charleston to Jarbidge in good traveling weather. The road, built over the two summits was hazardous because the snow stayed eight months of the year and drifts ranged from ten to twenty-five feet deep. In mid-winter and early spring, snowslides were almost a daily occurrence. A force of fifteen men worked constantly, clearing the road after these slides.

The passengers were given an unexpected fright as the stage did some steep climbing to pass over these summits. At the slightest concussion the snow could start down the mountainside. It was an exciting spectacle to see a small patch of snow break away from the edge of the road, move slowly at first and gain in momentum until it seemed the whole side of the mountain was sliding into the valley below, crashing through the pine forest and throwing a cloud of snow into the air in which were intermingled huge limbs of broken trees. Reverberations of the roaring, grinding sound lasted minutes after the avalanche had come to rest. But it was a different story when the slides started above the road, and the roar chilled the heart of the bravest, not knowing if the stage was in the path of the oncoming snow. The passengers gave a sigh of relief when they saw the snow shoot over the road either in front or behind them.

On one certain trip out of Jarbidge, the stage was loaded with a heavy consignment of mail, together with five passengers, one of them a woman. On traveling the narrow road cut into the mountainside near Danger Point, the stage was caught in one of those snowslides and narrowly escaped being swept down into the valley. Knowing that the stage was about due, the workmen saw the edge of the slide hit the vehicle. They climbed through the mass of twisted timbers and found the party huddled together. Luckily no one had been injured. The horses were unhitched, and the lady together with the stage driver and two passengers mounted horses. The driver took the first-class mail and all were piloted up around the slide to the road beyond and started for the first house which was a Charleston Ranch.

They arrived chilled and aching, especially those who were unaccustomed to mounts. After a short interval of rest, the horses were hitched to another stage and the journey was resumed to Deeth taking the mail and passengers. The two abandoned men were cared for by the roadbuilders at their tent on the mountain top. They were picked up by a team sent from Charleston the same day, and taken to the railroad by the next regular stage.

CHAPTER 19

A prospector snowshoed for twenty-five miles from Charleston to Jarbidge, passed over two summits and staked his claim. He called it the Long Hike. It was located high up on the mountainside just above the new gold camp.

Little was accomplished in the way of development of the Long Hike until the year of 1915 when a mining engineer enlisted some capital and opened up an ore body. Soon it was sold to the Elkoro Mines Company, a Guggenheim Corporation. Many claims bordering the Long Hike claim, one being Will Martin's Starlight, were bought by the Elkoro.

The company, at the cost of nearly a quarter of a million dollars, built a seventy-three mile electric power line from Buhl, Idaho. The power was generated at Thousand Springs, Idaho, and delivered 44,000 volts, available to all the mines and mills in the district at rates fixed by Idaho statutes. The Elkoro Company simultaneously began designing a treatment plant, which during the summer and winter of 1917 and spring of 1918 resulted in the building of the Elkoro Mill. The mill began operation in March of the year 1918, and ran steadily, treating daily about one hundred tons of ore. In June of 1919, the Elkoro was the largest producer of gold in Nevada.*

The mine and mill were well equipped. A seventeen hundred foot cable-drawn inclined tram connected the dormitories and mine-camp with the mill at the Jarbidge riverside and the town. The ore was delivered from the mines to the mill in two aerial trams with buckets, each holding one-third of a ton.

The mill employed the cyanidation and counter-current decantation process, using a combination of Marcy and Harding Mills with Blake Crusher and Dorr Classifiers. It had a rated capacity of one hundred tons in twenty-four hours but generally handled one hundred and twenty tons with ease, as most of the ore was soft. The small amount of ore which was hard and tended to cause undue wear in the steel lining of the ball mill, was crushed in a five-stamp adjunct. The mill made exceptionally good recoveries, the average extraction being about ninety-eight to

---

United States Geological Survey by Frank C. Schrader — 1923. Production of this mine brought to Nevada and the world another $10 million in gold and silver.

Different views of Elkoro and its relation to the Townsite

ninety-nine and one-half per cent of the gold and seventy-five per cent of the silver.

The Elkoro Mining Company employed about one hundred men in the early years of operation and used more than 40,000 pounds of supplies yearly. The mine timber was logged from Deer Creek, Bear Creek and various sawmills west of Jarbidge. It was sawed into timber lengths at the mine portal sawmill.

Underground explorations were carried on extensively by the Guggenheim controlled Elkoro Mines Company within their holdings, which resulted in finding sufficient ore to keep the mill running at full capacity continuously for fourteen and one-half years.*

Several years had gone by since Jack arrived in the Jarbidge gold camp. People wasted little time getting a town built. Stores, saloons, assay offices, restaurants and other businesses were operating. Hotels sprang up, two story and even one three-story with a balcony built off of the second floor overlooking main street. Tall, false fronts adorned many of the buildings. A movie house ran four nights a week.

---

*A survey was made by Smith and Stoddard, engineers for the Nevada State Bureau of Mines in the year of 1932; assisted by O.H. Hershey, geologist for the Elkoro —.

86

The town blacksmith shod the horses and mules, repaired wagon wheels and shrunk the iron bands to fit. The gambler dealt cards, the bartender served whiskey and mopped the crude counter.

Mines were developed and stamp mills constructed. Prospectors rode their horses or walked up the mountains and into the gulches and craters. Dumps of yellowish-tan ground dotted the hillsides, boulders and silt of the same various shades slid down to the river bed. Looked like a large gopher had been at work and moved on and on to other places, looking for something—. Men dug into the mountain, crushed the rocks and earth to a dust and panned it so carefully resulting in a fine string of yellow-tan gold.

Sawmills were working fast to supply the needs of the district. Supply wagons traveled the routes as often as was possible. The unbridled seven-day-a-week bustle and turbulence of a gold strike continued unbroken.

Jack was working hard to make a living for his family. The expected bonanza had not materialized yet, but he was an apt student. He learned the assaying routine, watched and copied the methods of seasoned miners tunneling into the depths of the mountainside, hungrily breaking the rocks and earth with drilled holes filled with explosive dynamite.

Jack thought — I am glad that I could afford to let Hattie and the two girls have a few weeks in California that winter. Away from the severe and long cold season we have here in Pavlak. Even though Gracie had to stay out of school one year. She was seven when she started in the first grade. Glad Hattie visited her sister and my folks there in California.

Maybe Jack was trying to console his conscience. He knew Hattie had been working hard and had so few conveniences. Now, I know that I should put running water into the house, he thought aloud, because it's so difficult for her to break the ice in the winter and carry a bucket of water from the river. And, I'm glad I bought that washing machine for her, even though Gracie has to turn the crank to keep it going. Good for children to have their chores after school or on Saturday. Hattie did come from California much happier with a more contented attitude.

Jack stopped his faithful horse to let him blow on the steep climb to the mine, at the same time he filled his pipe and lit it. The bay broke off some tall, wild grass that was growing beside the trail and the chomping of the bit sounded in the still air as he chewed the sweet grass. Jack looked down to the mill and overhead a tram bucket filled with ore for the stamp mill process was moving along the cable. The trail zig-zagged up the mountain passing under the tramline in places. The Bluster Mill and Mine was running full shifts.

Bluster Mine with Roy Cook ·

A striped chipmunk ran across the trail — the horse automatically started up the hill when he was rested, and Jack's thoughts raced on. There was excitement of uncovering a rich ore vein with a round of shots one day, yet he experienced the fear and awe when he walked into the tunnel piercing the side of the mountain, or looked down a deep shaft that he expected to descend. He was familiar with the mine's strange sounds, the dripping of water, the groan of timber supporting tons of earth. And just last night, when he returned home from work he had told Hattie:

88

"I'm sure that mountain moved last night, Kid, (his pet name for Hattie) a light quake or vibration, because some of my tools were almost covered with the overhanging dirt when I got to work this morning." And she had warned him again, as she was afraid also, yes — so afraid.

He thought of the ring of the pick against the rock, the single jack against the drill bit or an air jackhammer with that short, fast chatter-rat-a-tat-tat as the miner drilled for a charge of dynamite. The strange sights coming from the weird designs of ore formations. Apparitions appear to the hardened miner as well as the superstitious visitor.

He thought of the danger of a missed hole or "sleeper" detonating unexpectedly, cave-ins, explosions and other dreaded disasters. He remembered that day in the mill when he emptied a sack of cyanide and shook the sack a little to see that it had all dropped out into the tank. He had breathed the fumes unknowingly, then how he staggered for a second until he got a breath of fresh air. How dangerous it was, and his two children were standing nearby.

In the nice warm days of the summer, Mamma, Grace and I walked to the mill. We watched the mill in operation and talked to our friend, Bob McVicker. He was

Ten Stamp Mill

89

head millman. Always inquisitive, I asked, "Why is a mill built on the hillside, Bob, so you have so many steps to climb all day long?"

"Mills were always constructed on a sloping hillside to get the use of gravity. The ore goes from one operation to another," replied Bob.

We watched the tram buckets bring the ore from the mine and dump it in a large bin. It passed over a grizzly screen and the finer ore and small rocks were allowed to pass through, but the big rocks slid off into a crusher. After they went through the crusher and became mill-size they dropped back into the main chute with the fine ore and fell into the stamps. The stamps lifted up and down and turned as they lifted, pulverizing the ore. As water flowed into the stamps, the splash forced the fine substance through a screen at the front which was covered with a canvas apron. It next flowed over a copper plate covered with a coating of mercury (quicksilver). The tailings or waste passed over the mercury which caught the gold and silver.

When the ore got clogged and the stamps dropped on bare metal, the sound was deafening and Bob had to run up and down those narrow wooden steps to unclog the stoppage. I wondered how Bob and his crew could stand that constant noise.

This day we asked Mamma if we could ride up the tram to see Papa.

"We will have to ask Bob and he might telephone, but I wonder if we should do that, it might be dangerous?"

"I can call the brakeman at the headhouse of the mine," said Bob. "You can surprise your Papa. We have never had an accident with this tram and expect none."

So Bob loaded us all in one bucket and started us on our way. Grace and I thought it was so much fun, but I'm sure Mamma was really afraid.

"Don't be afraid, Mamma," begged Grace. "Bob told us that these buckets are clamped to the big cable above our heads and the loader man at the mine headhouse has a brake that he controls. You remember seeing that big wheel the cable goes around when the bucket is filled with ore? We are almost there."

As we passed over the tram towers the bucket took us high off the ground, then as we swung between the towers we went nearer the ground and over the scrub mahogany. It tickled my stomach. The loaded buckets passed us on their way down to the ore chute. When we reached the headhouse, the man held the bucket for us and Grace and I scampered out while he helped Mamma to her feet. Mamma said, "I'll not do that again, I'm glad we are here safely, but I guess the girls did enjoy the ride."

We went on to the mine portal, just a short climb away. There we found Papa just coming out with a mine car of ore. He was glad to see us, and surprised. Grace begged that we might go back into the cool tunnel with him. He finally consented but said that each of us was to have a carbide lamp when we went into the mine.

"Yes, Gracie, you all can go back with me this time, but I can't take very long. You know I'm a busy man."

He helped us fill our double-compartment carbide lamps, putting water dipped from a barrel into the top compartment and little grey pellets of calcium carbide in the lower one. The water dripping through an adjustable valve onto the carbide produced a gas. Papa explained to us that was why it hissed out of the lamp's jet and ignited with a pop when we sparked the flint wheels with our thumbs.

90

He said, "The pointed yellow flame is our only weapon against the dark of the tunnel. Sometime the gas jets clog and I have to clean them with this needlelike sliver of steel called a reamer. Every miner carries his reamer in a small metal tube, buttoned in his shirt pocket. A man's life may depend on producing light in a hurry."

We walked into the cold, drafty, damp tunnel and already were chilled. We stepped over the rusty tracks and slipped into little puddles of oozing water. Often a drip of water or two fell on our heads or face from the ceiling. The lamps cast long scissor-like shadows of our legs along the tunnel walls. Finally we came to the first station, as Papa called it. It was like a small room with tunnels taking off from it in three directions. Men were working in the side tunnels and in a raise which went up or a shaft or stope which went down. The water dropped and dripped — ploomp, ploomp, ploomp — and the sound gave back an echo. We turned the corner and started into another tunnel. It seemed to get darker, almost overwhelming, then a thought came to me how it would be without the sunlight, the trees, the stars and moon and the feel of space. How could men work in this pit of darkness? Even though I was just a youth I was feeling the sense of being closed in and was happy to see the daylight as we came out on the Success dump.

"Why, Papa! We went in the Bluster tunnel and came out the Success tunnel," I said.

"Yes, my dears, they've been working hard to drive that tunnel through this mountain; when we turned that corner was when we started out this way," Papa told us.

"Well, the day is over for me, and I am ready to go home."

"Have you a horse for Helen and me, Jack, to ride home? Grace can ride behind you on bay Dick," said Hattie.

"Yes, we will borrow Scotty's horse for you. He is gentle and I will bring him back in the morning."

As the horses ambled down the steep trail the sun was setting over the summit across the canyon. The river below splashed and fell over boulders and dead trees and the echoing sound came closer as we neared the bottom of the mountainside.

We rode in and out of the pine trees, into stands of aspen and then into the gnarled and fuzzy-tipped, short mahoganies, passed fragrant, wild honeysuckle flowers and Indian paint brush.

When we reached home we were all glad. It had been a busy day and I, for one, had learned much.

CHAPTER 20

"Now, Jack, I want to enter Stockings in the horse race on the Fourth of July celebration in Jarbidge. Can we ask Pete, that small cowboy, to ride him?"

"If you'd like to. Do you think you want to let your pet horse run against those horses that will come from Martin's horse range or the Diamond A Ranch?" Jack didn't want to discourage Hattie, but feared she might be disappointed if Stockings didn't win or was hurt. He knew there would be some wild young mustangs with rough riders among them.

"Yes, I want to show them my beautiful, white-faced bay; that he can run and that he will win. With a good, lightweight rider like Pete Turner, I'll bet he can win. The purse is one hundred dollars, but that isn't the most important thing, although I could use that too. I know Stockings can do it, against any horse around here. I tried him out on the loping stretch coming home from Jarbidge the other day. He had such a burst of speed and I could tell that he had lots of reserve. Mrs. Ross came running up behind me on her golden-colored palamino and Stockings wouldn't let him pass. Of course I didn't have the children with me. He is like an old plug when one or both of the girls are riding. You'd never know how smart he is, Jack." Hattie continued with her head held high and an expression of pride on her face.

Jack smiled and thought, how she loved that horse and, really, Stockings loved her and the children, that was evident. He had seen Gracie taking many chances of being kicked or stepped on but the bay just stood sleepy-like.

"Why don't you ride him, Kid?" Jack jokingly asked Hattie.

They laughed about such an idea, but secretly Hattie wished she could ride her prized beauty and show him off.

"I'll get Pete to ride Stockings on the Fourth for you." Jack reassured Hattie. "He's already told me he would like to ride the bald-face."

The next day Mamma curried and groomed Stockings until his coat glistened in the sunlight. Grace helped her while I sat and watched. Mamma had spent all her savings from the sugar bowl to buy a beautiful braided horse-hair bridle, hand-made by a prisoner in the penitentiary. A cowhand came through the town and gambled all his money away on the poker table and even lost the bridle to the gambler in the Mint Bar. Mr. Griffin just knew Mamma would like that bridle so he sold it to her to get his money back. What would a gambler do with a horse-hair bridle, he thought.

The Fourth of July was celebrated with frontier excitement. The day was introduced with blasts of dynamite, set off from nearby points on the hillsides. Day and night celebrations progressed from the early morning flag raising until the complete fatigue of the fifth. There was foot racing of all descriptions for children and adults, also the amusing sack race and the familiar tug of war.

Then came the trick riding which was always a spectacular sight. Tom Beeson was one of the best around and had a well-trained horse, and later rode a burro, doing tricks from his back. Still more ostentatious was the Roman-horse-riding. One man literally stood on two horses and held the reins of each horse while the animals ran evenly together up the main street. This was a feat of beauty, skill and perfect balance. But of course the horses had to be trained to run evenly and they did.

As usual there was the single and double jackhammer contest. But the horse races were the highlight of the day for us. One excitable animal bolted between the buildings in the middle of a group of spectators. We were sitting in a wagon and I was frightened. Stockings was entered with some fine saddle bred horses. He started with lots of speed but got pushed behind about half way up the middle of the street. They ran from the lower end of town to the upper part, about one mile in distance. Pete waited until he had a good opening and then gave Stockings his head and a few kicks with his heels, a couple of quick whip lashes on the front shoulder and Mamma's prize horse ran like a streak. Those long legs went into a running stride and passed all the other horses, finishing at least four lengths ahead.

We saw some money change hands and knew that bets were made on the horse races.

Following the races and the contests, the ladies held their chuck wagon dinner. Then some of the citizenry moved into the saloons and the pianola could be heard and the scratching of heavy miners' shoes on the rough floors. However others dressed for the more sedate dance of the night at the Commercial Hall where no liquor was consumed. There a fiddler, piano player and accordionist provided the music for dancing.

How Grace and I loved those dances because the hall was always festive-looking and the floor waxed to a mirror shine. Bob McVicker and Uncle Will danced the first two or three dances with us. They said we were good dancers like our mother and that we learned fast. Soon we were asleep in one of the big chairs and covered with a robe or coat and sometime 'way after midnight we four bundled into a wagon and went home to Pavlak.

When Wilma and Muriel, two of our favorite school chums, came from town to play with us, we found the cool of the river water inviting on a hot summer's day. On one such visit in July, we waded around the edge of the river which ran close to the cabin's front porch. We followed down the river where it widened into a pool of deeper water and was covered with tree limbs and protruding willows which cast their shadows on the clear water's smooth sandstone bottom. On the bank, under the willows, we removed our clothes and waded in, screeching as the cold water came up around our tummies. After a while we got used to the cold and screamed and splashed. Mamma told us later that she could hear us and we didn't sound like young ladies, but like rough boys.

The sun shone through the leaves, lacy and warm, and after we came out of the water and rubbed ourselves dry with the towels, which Mamma had provided, our firm bodies glowed pink. We dressed and went back to the house and the backyard.

94

"Let's ride Pinkie," said Gracie. Pinkie, a female burro so fat and harmless, raised her head and brayed at us.

"Let's go up the road and visit Mrs. McVicker," Wilma said.

"Maybe Pinkie doesn't want to go up the road" Muriel knew that Pinkie usually went when she wanted to and not when riders chose.

Helen broke off a small willow. "We can switch ha' on the butt."

"Helen! where do you pick up words like that!"

"F'om you kids. Jacie, (since I couldn't pronounce the "r" of the alphabet yet, I said the word the best possible way eliminating the r) put a halta' on Pinkie and help me up."

Grace haltered the sleepy burro and lifted me onto her back, then said, "Come on, there's room for all of us." Wilma climbed up behind me and Muriel behind her. Gracie wanted to get on in front so that she could guide Pinkie. There seemed to be no room for her so she told us all to slide back and she got a box and slipped onto the shoulders of the burro. Muriel, afraid of sliding off the rounded rear-end of Pinkie, hung on to her sister Wilma for dear life.

We nudged the burro with our black-stockinged knees, kicked with our heels and clucked and howled, but Pinkie moved only when she wanted to and just as fast. She ambled up the road toward the steep pathway which led to Mrs. McVicker's home but that was as far as she would go. Since Muriel was about to be unseated from the rear of the donkey, we thought it best to turn around and head for home. Pinkie liked that and went at a much faster pace, probably thinking she would get rid of that load when reaching the house, which she did.

On special occasions, such as Grace's birthday in midsummer, Mamma let us take her Victrola and a few records to the yard for music and dancing. We dressed up and played partners, one a girl and the other would be a boy.

Our summer days expanded with a beautiful life for children. Some days we went horse hunting — took bridles and climbed the hills, walked the road, to find Stockings and Badgie, Grace's beloved palomino pony. Stockings seemed to know Badgie was small and couldn't take care of himself around other horses who bit and kicked, so Stockings went after them with ears back and teeth bared. He cared for Badgie as he would a pony-child.

In summertime, wild flowers came to the tables in jars or vases. Mamma's geraniums and begonias bloomed in the windows in gallon cans serving as pots. She had her prized reds and pinks and they could also be taken outside a few days and nights of the short summers.

The kitchen served as a bathroom for the weekly tub baths which Mamma gave us. There was no need for the chamber pot in the summers; we went out to the toilet before going to bed. Grace always had to go with me. I was afraid of the dark and she knew that, so just as we started to return to the house she would say, "Helen, there's a bear." I'd run to the house as fast as my legs would take me while she stood laughing.

Splitting wood and kindling for the two stoves and getting it into the woodboxes in the house seemed to be an endless chore. Carrying buckets of water from the river into the kitchen was what Mamma disliked the most. How she wished we had the water piped into the house from the river. Papa usually filled both buckets before he went to work in the early mornings, but they never lasted long. In the winter, when the river was iced over, Mamma had to break the ice at the edge to fill the buckets. And on that same ice, we liked to skate.

About dusk, one bright moonlight evening after the chickens had gone to roost in the chickenhouse, we heard them squawking.

"Mercy! What's all that racket! My chickens," cried Mamma.

Upon running out we found a weasel hunting his dinner in the chickenhouse.

Mamma was proud of her hens. She had Plymouth Rocks, Rhode Island Reds and Buff Orpington for the good baking chickens. The weasel ran away without taking a meal with him.

Papa was a vivid and concise storyteller and we loved to have him picture the beauty of Colorado and Wyoming. His memory held suspenseful tales of bear and cougar and beautiful animals of the wilderness.

He often imitated the growls and actions of the wild beasts with startling realism, while Grace and I listened and watched intently. The heroic life he had led made him wonderful, so we thought. We knew him to be a perfect marksman with a rifle and in physical combat capable of holding his own with any antagonist of his weight. While not a large man, he was nearly six feet in height and had courage and endurance.

Papa gathered us on his knees at night before the fire and told us of the horses he had owned and cared for, about his mother, sisters and brothers and about his short home life as a young boy.

"People are moving away," Hattie said to Jack, "and not taking their organ. I only wish we could afford to buy one, Gracie would like it so much, especially since she is taking piano lessons from Faye."

The next day, as if in answer to her wish, Hattie saw a team of horses and wagon pull up in front of the house. Two men were unloading the lovely little organ, a foot pedal pump instrument.

"That can't be for us," Hattie exlaimed so excitedly. She and Grace would not believe it until they were assured by the men who said, "Jack Goodwin paid for it and asked us to bring it to the house. It is yours."

"Goodie, goodie!" screamed Gracie and she jumped up and down for joy. "Mamma, Mamma, look what Papa bought for us! Now I can practice my lessons and I can sing too."

Hattie thought what a nice surprise, how thoughtful her husband was since the mine was not producing well just then. It pleased her to see that the one daughter liked music as she, herself did. There would be time for the little daughter later.

She hurried into the house to make room for the men to put the organ. It was heavy and required a lot of pulling and pushing to get it through the narrow doorway into the living room. Grace and I went in to watch and could hardly wait for the men to leave, anxious to try out this odd-shaped instrument. Mamma explained the foot pedals and the stops. She said, "Now girls, you have to pump the pedals and pull the certain stops then play the keys. You can raise or lower the stool by turning the top around. Understand?"

"Yes, Mamma, please let me try now." Grace was nearly bursting with enthusiasm and joy.

But, of course, when I tried to pump the pedals, my legs weren't long enough to reach them easily. Nevertheless, it wasn't long before my legs had grown enough to manipulate the organ — and my fingers slipped over the keys hitting discordant chords, and Hattie heard, but as long as I was enjoying it what did it matter.

Hattie cleaned and polished the wood, scrubbed the keys "to get the smell of whiskey and tobacco and remove the dirty finger prints," she said; and put some vases of flowers from her garden in the two little places intended for some object of decoration. The mirror, connected to the top of the organ, she cleaned until it shimmered and sparkled. The beautiful oak grain of the wood shone like nothing we'd ever seen. It was a grand instrument and such a nice addition to our home.

Mamma loved to work in the post office and when she was extra busy Grace would help her. The Pavlak Post Office, a sod roof, one-room, log cabin was on the opposite side of the Jarbidge River from our house, reached by a foot bridge.*

---

*The Pavlak Post Office was established on December 14, 1915 and James Hayes was appointed as Postmaster. But upon his resignation about a year later, my Mamma, Hattie Goodwin, became postmaster.

CHAPTER 21

It was my first year of school, the first grade, and I liked school. Mrs. Nelson taught all eight grades which were included in the one large room. I clung to my sister Grace. As I couldn't pronounce the 'r' of the alphabet, I called her "Jacie." The older boys chided her about that, which made her unhappy.

Grace was old enough to have her own horse. Therefore Badgie, a beautiful and gentle palomino pony, took us to and from school. When the weather was too cold to leave Badgie tied so long during school hours, Papa took us in the sleigh or we walked the two miles from Pavlak to Jarbidge. Some days when I came home tired and crying, Mamma would not let me go back the next day.

"What is the matter with my little Helen?" she would ask.

"Those older girls wouldn't *jag* their feet and make a *chail*," I cried.

"No!" Gracie said laughingly. "That isn't the way it is at all, Mamma. Helen wants to go first and break through the soft, new snow and she gets tired."

Our Christmas was a gay and plentiful one. The children spent hours rehearsing a play, singing in a chorus and learning poems to recite. The show was given in the Commercial Clubhouse and the attending crowd filled the hall. A large decorated tree stood on the floor at one side of the stage. The pine tree, cut from the forest, reached twelve feet into the rafters of the building. The Club had purchased and wrapped a little package for every school child and preschool child in town.

Tom Beadle, dressed as Santa, presented the gifts as he called the names of the children. He made a folksy, jolly Santa who laughed heartily and often. He had a big tummy so didn't have to use pillows to round out his shape.

Grace played a short selection she had learned while taking piano lessons, also sang a solo. I was so shy, but finally told one little rhyme:

>Jane ate cake
>Jane ate jelly
>Jane went to bed with a pain in her —
>Now, don't get excited, don't be filled with dread.
>Jane went to bed with a pain in her head.

Our Christmas at home was loving and a bright time in our lives. My doll, a German baby-doll, had a porcelain head with eyes that rolled around and legs that curled like those of a real baby. She had dresses and diapers too. My first good doll and I loved her.

"Hilda will break if you drop her, Helen," warned Mamma, "so take good care of her." The name Hilda, the year and company who made her, were pressed into the porcelain at the back of her neck.

"I will, Mamma." I hugged my doll and sat rocking her.

Bear Creek hill was at its best in winter from November until the last big snow storm in April. Children of all ages flocked there to coast. Smaller children bundled in heavy coats and red stocking caps stopped on their way to and from school to slide just once or twice, or to make pictures in the feathery snow. Older children coasted over the ice-slick run on sleds of all descriptions. And when the big boys yelled, "Clear the track!" everyone scattered from the slide and watched breathlessly as the dangerous double-rippers flashed by, swaying, bounding, crossing the main street of Jarbidge to come to stop just before crashing into Brauning's candy store.

One late afternoon after the school hours, Grace and I were among the many town kids on the Bear Creek slide. Papa and Mamma had warned Grace to be careful, that her sled was one of the fastest made. It was named 'The Flyer' with round runners that collapsed under the sled for easy carrying. It could accommodate three upright comfortably or one lying down. My sled was smaller and slower, but fast enough for me.

Alongside the slick were banks of both loose and packed snow. Newton Cranston had just gone down the slide and run into one of the packed snow banks. The sharp pointed runners of his sled were protruding into the runway.

Bobby Kendall was next to come and after his yell "Clear the Track" he ran and belly-flopped on his fast sled getting a speed of lightning to enter the slide. It was too late when we called for him to Stop! Don't Go! He ran into the stalled sled before anyone realized what was happening. The pointed runners entered his temple, killing him instantly.

That was a sad night for the Kendall family, the residents of Jarbidge and the school chums of a boy who was well-liked. Bobby was the youngest of five children. His parents and the family lived in Jarbidge many years and also owned a business.

CHAPTER 22

The winter of 1916 heavy snowfalls piled up to dangerous depths. Crippen Grade, just two miles from Jarbidge, Nevada, was the most perilous it had been since its completion two years before. With the wind blowing and the snow drifting on the narrow, twisting road, drivers never knew when they were too near the treacherous edge.

"Just last week a freight wagon and team went over the bank, falling many feet," said Mr. Jewel Martin. "A two horse team fell over the side and the horses were killed. They were fighting to get up and one fell on top of the other. Both had heads down in the snow and wouldn't quit kicking. When they do that, why, you have a dickens of a time to keep them from smothering each other.

"I'm the one who put the horses over the grade the first time the Elkoro Company sent me out, after they bought a lot of extra mining property in Jarbidge," Jewel continued. "They sent me out to the railroad station at Deeth, Nevada. I got up to Danger Point on the Jarbidge-Charleston road and put the leaders over the grade. They didn't get hurt or killed that time though.

"Jarbidge was a busy town with all the mines running and Guggenheims getting started on the Elkoro Mine and Mill. I was only a young man then. A gambler named Sully who wanted to help me took me into Johnny Cost's restaurant and said, 'Johnny, you know me, don't you?'

" 'Yes, I do, Sully.'

" 'You know I pay my bills? Give this young man his meals until he gets a job and put it on my bill.'

" 'Gamblers are all 'like — today it is chicken and tomorrow feathers, so today I have some chicken and I can help you,' said Sully."

Fred M. Searcy, a young unmarried man of thirty years, was apprehensive as he drove the mail stage on his inbound trip to Jarbidge from Three Creek, Idaho, December 5, 1916.

I wish I was over this Crippen Grade and into Jarbidge, thought Fred. Never saw such a driving snowstorm. And when that team went over the grade a few days ago, they sure tore this road up getting the wagon and supplies out.

100

Fred talked to his two-horse team, kept a tight rein and used extra precaution, as the horses slowly found their footing in the snow on the narrow road. The stage was actually a small, open express wagon built to carry six hundred pounds.

The mail outfit finally reached the bottom of the grade and continued up the canyon to Jarbidge.

With a sigh Searcy thought, That's over. He noticed the fast approaching dusk and estimated it to be about five o'clock. Now I only have a short distance and I'm on time. He could travel a little faster now, but still the horses could not go much more than a brisk walk.

The snow erupted into comet-like forms as it fell and large dry flakes stuck to his eyebrows and lashes. His breath made a vapor in the cold air. It had been a rough trip.

That was payday for the men in the mines and mills. They had their checks to cash. The nine saloons in the little mining camp were packed on that night of December fifth.

The crackling and popping of wood-gorged heating stoves, the resounding of silver dollars and whiskey glasses and the scuffing of heavy boots mingled in the crowded, too few establishments. Stovepipes rattled and windows and doors shook as the icy wind whistled down the canyon. Snow blew in the doors when men entered, shivered, and flicked their hats and Mackinaws.

Men were waiting for the mail stage which carried approximately $3200 in small bills to be delivered to Crumley and Walker, owners of the Success Saloon and Restaurant. Also awaited were funds for others expecting certain amounts and a cashier's check of $1000 for Brauning, the candy store operator.

When the stage had not arrived by nine o'clock, Postmaster John Scott Fleming became uneasy about the fate of the mail and the money in it so he passed the word around. Mrs. Dexter heard this and telephoned the postmaster that she saw the stage pass her house about five o'clock. She called to the driver, "Fred, aren't you about frozen?" He did not reply. He was humped up on the seat with his coat collar turned up, she said, the snow was coming down and the wind blowing so badly that she couldn't see clearly.

Just a few hundred yards farther on, some freighters, Campbell, Connors and Peterson brothers, were taking care of their corraled animals. Campbell knew Fred and when he got the news the stage had not arrived at the post office he went to tell Fleming the stage had passed within a hundred feet of him, that he called out, "Hello Kid!" But received no answer. "I thought, perhaps, the poor lad was so nearly frozen that he drove right on to the post office and then to the stage barn."

It was then Postmaster Fleming suspected foul play and formed a searching party.

The night was bitter cold. Lighted by kerosene lanterns, searchers went to the bridge, about twelve hundred feet north of the post office. The wind raged, blew the snow into their faces as they plunged knee-deep into newly fallen layers that covered the old. They looked over the brush-covered bottom from the bridge to where the freighters were camped without finding any sign of the team or wagon. They went back and started over. The men spread out and trudged on, their lighted lanterns giving a blur of reflections across the white vastness and along the river bank. Now and then the wind whipped up the snow and drove it against the willows. Their lights revealed a small cabin near the river. The tin roof rattled and creaked as though it would blow away.

The cold sent plumes of breath from the men's mouth. Freezing night air reddened their cheeks, chilled their gloved hands and stung their eyes. A few of the older men began to fall yards behind, some went back to town to continue the search in the morning while they grumbled about the deep snow, extreme cold and hindrance of darkness.

Young Neale Hendryx, a twenty-two year old miner, was first to come upon the spot where the dim, snow-covered wagon and horses' tracks turned off the new road onto the old one that had been used to ford the river nearer the middle of the town before the bridge was built. And it was Hendryx who peered ahead, called out, and gestured toward a clump of willows barely visible in the night. The search party came behind Hendryx, found the barely visible tracks and the willows. By then Neale saw Searcy's mail stage and his team headed into the clump of willows, where the team would be likely to stand, and had stood for five hours.

"Whoa, boy, whoa − easy −" he didn't want to frighten the horses with the loud talk and sudden flash of lights.

The dead body of Fred Searcy was sprawled on the seat where he usually sat to drive, on the right-hand side next to the brake, leaning over and resting partly on the seat. Three inches of snow covered the slain man. The team was still hitched to the wagon, cold and snow-covered. Two of the searching party worked the horses and wagon out of the brush and drove to the post office.

The searchers found two of the second-class mail sacks, which had been slit open and part of the papers and small packages scattered about the snow. This explained the bloody packages which Hattie Goodwin received at the Pavlak Post Office. And the Christmas gifts from mail-order stores coming to the Goodwin children, other children and residents in the Jarbidge District.

However, the searchers didn't find the first class mail sacks which contained the money. They did see men's and dog's tracks in the old snow covered by the newly fallen snow.

Although some of the men kept following the barely visible tracks until early morning, they finally gave up to wait for daylight. The storm had slackened and another few hours would give the constable, justice of the peace, postmaster and eager citizens a little rest.

Since there were dog tracks at the scene, Mr. J.T. McCormick, owner of a general mercantile store, and an experienced hunter with dogs, had a theory that it might be well to watch the dogs of the town. He had carefully examined the dog tracks in the snow by blowing out the light snow and obtaining a good print underneath. From this clue McCormick found the track was made by a large dog so he watched the dogs around town the next morning.

A friendly tramp dog had, for the last few months, attached himself to one certain gambler and when the dog missed his master in town he must have tracked him by scent to the framed tent house, then across the bridge and had arrived at the scene when the murderer pulled the horses to a stop at the willows and leaped from the wagon.

By ten o'clock that morning, McCormick knew he had the right dog spotted and thought that it might go back over the trail if the animal was taken to the spot. He coaxed the friendly, old dog with a bone and put a rope around his neck. He then led the dog to the scene of the night before. Upon letting the critter loose, he started for the bridge actually sniffing an almost snow-hidden trail. He led them to the edge of the bridge where a first class, brass-locked mail sack lay, partly covered with snow. The knife, which had evidently cut open the sack, was laying among the bloodsmeared letters which were scattered through the snow. Registered mail containing the $3200 was gone. Loose letters had been examined and those from the bank were torn open. There was one letter with a bloody palm print addressed to Miss Gladys Pangborn (later Mrs. Jewel Martin).

Tucked away under the bridge between two stringers, searchers Mr. and Mrs. Alexander Chisholm found a black coat. Chisholm pulled it out and his wife called to the officers. The coat had a considerable amount of blood on the bottom. On looking further they found a small canvas sack tucked over the pier under the middle of the bridge. This sack which was supposed to contain $200 in silver for Newton Crumley and Walker Success Bar had only $180. Possibly the $20 had been taken for spending money.

Circumstances directed to the arrest of Ben Kuhl, a gambler and part-time cook at the boardinghouse of the O.K. Mine. The overcoat was believed to be his and the dog followed Kuhl, usually staying with the gambler in his tent near the bridge where the coat was found. Constable I.C. Hill and Deputy Sheriff Dave Marquardson searched Kuhl's tent and found a .44 caliber pistol which had one cartridge fired. A blood-stained shirt found between Kuhl's tent and the river showed laundry marks said to be like those which were found on other laundry belonging to him.

Ben Kuhl had been regarded unfavorably in Jarbidge because he attempted to jump the claim of a lot next to the post office bought by Oscar and Hayes. They moved a small cabin from it and had cleared the land to build a pool hall. Owing to lack of lumber, work was not started but a notice of ownership stating that a building would be there soon was put on the lot. That night Ben Kuhl put a tent on the property and said he owned it. He was arrested for trespassing and acted as his own attorney. During the trial he was fined fifty dollars for contempt of court. He made remarks to the Judge about it being a "Kangaroo Court."

The coroner's inquest and preliminary trial was held by Jarbidge Justice of the Peace Yewell. Sheriff Joe Harris from Elko and a United States Deputy Marshall and post office detective assisted in the investigation.

Ben Kuhl, Edward Beck, otherwise known as "The Swede," and Billy McGraw, all gamblers, were held without bond and bound over to the Elko County grand jury. Another gambler, Jennings, and the woman with whom he was living were arrested on suspicion. After hearing the woman testify that she heard Kuhl and Beck plot to rob the mail stage, Jennings and his woman were released.

Swede Beck was a close friend of Billy McGraw, the man who a month ago borrowed the gun which was found in the Kuhl tent. McGraw borrowed the gun from "Poker George" but had been in the habit of leaving it with the bartender at the Success Saloon in the mornings and getting it nights. Early in the evening on which the murder took place, Beck went into the Success and asked McGraw to let him have the gun, saying Kuhl wanted it. They needed some meat and Kuhl might kill a deer. McGraw got the gun from the bartender and turned it over to "The Swede."

The next time Kuhl and Beck were seen in town was about eight o'clock when they went into Jack Griffin's Saloon and seemed anxious to have the men in the place notice that they were there. Kuhl called to all those in the saloon to have a drink and managed to refer to the time. He even asserted that he was up town playing cards all evening, but could find no one who would swear he had seen either man between 5:45 o'clock and the time they came into the saloon together. Kuhl's effort to call attention to himself is said by such establishment habitues to be different from his usual conduct and to have caused some comment at the time.

At the preliminary investigation, Kuhl denied all knowledge of the shooting and said that the overcoat was not his. A former partner, called "Turkey Curley" was brought in from the mine where he was working, said that at one time Kuhl had owned the overcoat but had given it to him. "Curley" also said that when he went to his mine he left the coat in the tent in which they both lived and which had since been occupied by Kuhl.

Kuhl took active part in the search when the alarm was given Tuesday night, the 5th of December. He must have gone to his tent and changed his clothes, walked up town and made his presence known. Then he joined in the hunt for the guilty fiend who had shot young Fred Searcy in the back without a fighting chance and left his victim soaked in frozen blood for five hours.

Ed Beck took the stand at the preliminary trial in Jarbidge and said he was thirty-three years old, born in Finland, had been in camp three months. For occupation worked and played poker. He said he was in the Log Cabin Saloon somewhat drunk early Tuesday evening when Kuhl came in and asked him to go outside where Kuhl then asked him for a gun. They went to the Success Saloon and Swede Beck asked McGraw for a gun which McGraw got from the bartender. He said after he got the gun from McGraw, he and Kuhl went across the street to the Palm saloon and went into the toilet where he gave the gun to Kuhl. Beck said that he went around town afterwards for a while and was playing poker in the Mint Saloon when the stage was held up. He did not see Kuhl again until after the killing had been done and then saw Kuhl and had a drink with him and Kuhl told him to keep quiet and he would split.

"I took time off to go to the investigation trial held in Jarbidge," said Jewel Martin. " 'The Swede,' Edward Beck was so scared. Billy McGraw had borrowed the gun from 'Poker George' and Beck asked McGraw to get it for him, that he wanted to give it to Ben Kuhl. Swede stood guard by the bridge. He gave the pistol to Kuhl. Beck said, " 'I give the gun to Kuhl, but he vasn't to kill 'im.' "*

Ben Kuhl took the chair, said he was thirty-one years old, born in Indiana, occupation poker player and worked when he could get a job. He had been here since May 18th. Kuhl denied making such statement to Beck. Also denied any

*Mr. Jewel Martin in conversation while visiting with the author.

knowledge of the crime. He agreed that Beck gave him the gun in the Log Cabin toilet to go hunting, but he was pretty drunk during the day so decided not to go.

Kuhl gave Beck one dollar to get shaved then walked up the street to buy a stove for his tent and found the store closed so went into the Northern Saloon to get a drink. He claimed that when he left there he went to the Log Cabin and played poker for three hours then went with Beck to have a bowl of chili. When he heard that the mail stage was missing he joined the searchers.

Kuhl told the Jarbidge investigators that he got up Wednesday morning about 10:30, put the gun in his pocket and went up town. Information got to him that all the rounders would be arrested, so he went to his tent and put the gun in the suitcase. He then went across the river to see what had been found and on returning, stopped at his tent and noticed that the coat was gone. "I had suspicions that it had been taken to implicate me, so when I was arrested I denied owning the coat or of owning any coat," said Kuhl. "When the tent was searched and the gun found, I acknowledged owning the coat." Kuhl denied knowing anything about the crime and did not want to be implicated in any way, also claimed that he could prove an alibi and that he did not get the gun until after the murder was committed.

McGraw waived making any statement.

The prisoners were held in the Jarbidge jail for several days. Elko County Sheriff Harris and prosecuting attorney took them to Elko, Nevada, on the train by way of Twin Falls, Idaho, and Ogden, Utah, since the route over the summits to Elko was closed by snowdrifts. United States Deputy Marshal remained at Jarbidge after the coroner's inquest and investigation.

None of the money was found except the $182 in the sack near the overcoat at the foot of the bridge. Nearly everyone in camp knew the money was expected at the Crumley and Walker Success Saloon and Restaurant. It had been delayed, but would be in on the Tuesday mail stage, so the robbers must have known when to expect its arrival.

Ben Kuhl, William McGraw and Edward Beck were held prisoners in the Elko County Jail for nine and one-half months until their trials came up in the district court. During this time the experts were working on a new line of evidence, new to the Nevada Courts and to the United States Courts; that of a palm print — and also the fact that the evidence was circumstantial. In view of this, each man was granted a separate trial. Since the evidence was practically the same for each case the court requested that nothing be published in the newspapers of the happenings and evidence of the first case as it would make it impossible to obtain a jury for the following two cases.

While searching through the sacks, the robber-murderer left his bloody palm print on an envelope. This was placed in charge of Sheriff Harris, who promptly communicated with C.H. Stone, Superintendent of the Bureau of Identification of the Bakersfield, California, Police Department. Mr. Stone was recognized as one of the foremost finger print experts and formerly had been connected with the Nevada State Police. On receiving the envelope containing the bloody print, Stone wrote Sheriff Harris that it was a portion of the left palm and that if he would send the prints of the three men suspected of the crime, he would make a comparison. This was done in the month of January, 1917. After a thorough examination Mr. Stone replied that the bloody print on the envelope was that of the prisoner Kuhl, and not that of Beck or McGraw.

When the district attorney's office decided to introduce this testimony in the Kuhl case, Mr. Stone was instructed to have pictures made of the palm print and this part of the work he assigned to O.W. Bottorff, Superintendent of the County Bureau of Identification at Fresno, California. Bottorff had made a specialty of enlargements and lantern slides of prints, besides being a leading expert on finger prints. The enlargements and negatives were made of the bloody print on the envelope and the one taken of Kuhl's palm, both being placed on the same plate so the comparisons could be made and seen by the jury.

At a convention and regular annual meeting of the Pacific Coast Finger Print Experts, the pictures of the two prints were submitted and each and every man unhesitatingly pronounced the two prints as having been made by the same palm. It was also passed on by other national finger print experts, who concurred with Mr. Stone in his decision.

Since Kuhl denied any knowledge of the crime, as he did through the district court trial as well as the investigation in Jarbidge, also because the use of a palm print as evidence was new in the courts of law, the experts had to go to extreme lengths to convince the court that the evidence was admissible. Ordinarily, in the comparison of finger prints, eight or nine distinctive features or peculiarities are all that is necessary to establish the fact that the prints are identical and made by the same person. But in the Kuhl palm print the experts had selected eighteen points of similarities for comparison, more than twice the regularly required number.

This was made possible by the fact that the bloody print on the envelope, which was the fleshy portion of the left hand, contained a particularly plain imprint of a "whorl," or "island," which was duplicated in the print of Kuhl's palm. The experts in testifying before the jury went into details in explaining every peculiarity and pointing out on the enlarged print every distinctive feature.

Mr. Stone, at the conclusion of his testimony, was asked by the State if he could make a positive statement as to the hand that made the imprint on both the envelope and the print of Kuhl's palm. He answered: "I am as positive as it is humanly possible to be positive of anything, as positive as I am that I am in this court room, that those two prints were made by the same hand."

Expert Bottorff illustrated his testimony by the means of a propectoscope. The court room was darkened and the pictures of the two prints were thrown on the screen, and every line was magnified many thousand times. He pointed out the lines and peculiarities and told the jury the history of finger prints and how they were used in the courts of every civilized nation of the earth. At the conclusion of his testimony he stated positively that the print on the envelope and the one made by Kuhl's palm were made by the same hand.

The legal battle between the attorneys on the admission of the palm print occupied the attention of the court for two days and was bitterly fought by the defense. With the jury excluded from the court room the two experts were placed on the stand and every detail was given to the court; the enlarged pictures of the print, the methods used in presenting the evidence to the jury and the testimony of the two experts — even more fully than was given to the jury — before Judge Taber would rule on the objections of the defendant. It was a most interesting part of the case and the court room was filled daily with men and women attracted by this unusual feature. This testimony was conceded to be the keystone of the State's case which had been built up with painstaking work by the district attorney's office, and which was needed to complete the chain of circumstantial evidence to fasten the crime on the defendant, Ben Kuhl.

Attorney E.E. Caine, counsel for the defense, fought for the life of his client heroically from the calling of the first juror to the end of the case, but he fought against desperate odds. He gave Kuhl the advantage of every technical point, and if he did lose would continue the fight for his life in higher courts.

The defense rested on the evening of October 4, 1917, and the next day the rebuttal by the State was concluded. The court read the instructions to the jury at two o'clock and District Attorney Carville opened the argument for the State, concluding the afternoon of October 5, 1917. He was followed by the defense the next morning, and Deputy District Attorney Cantwell finished for the State that night, then the case went to the jury.

In his argument to the jury, Attorney Caine clearly presented every scrap of evidence which might throw a reasonable doubt on the guilt of the defendant. His appeal to the jury not to convict on the evidence presented — purely circumstantial in nature — was a classic that will long be remembered by those present and who later read the records. Kuhl was given the advantage of being defended by one of the brightest legal minds in Nevada; nevertheless the evidence against him was overwhelming.

The closing argument for the State by Deputy District Attorney Cantwell was finished by 9 P.M. and the long fought case was given to the jury. When the jury's vote was taken by the foreman on the guilt or innocence of the accused — and the verdict was guilty, the next question to decide was the degree of punishment. On the first ballot the vote stood six to six on the extreme punishment. Then the principal evidence was reexamined by the jury, and after another ballot, the vote stood unanimous for the first degree.

Just as the clock struck the hour of midnight, Saturday, October 6, 1917, (ten months and one day after the tragedy in Jarbidge) the jury in the Kuhl murder case brought in a verdict. When Judge E.J.L. Taber took his seat and asked the foreman if a verdict had been reached, not a sound could be heard while the judge silently read the verdict and returned it to the clerk. The defendant was as cool and collected as he had been at any time during the trial, and when the clerk read the verdict, which could mean his death, not a visible tremor shook Kuhl's body. He seemed to care nothing for the findings of the jury. He had slept well throughout the night and his appearance did not show that he was worried.

The verdict read "guilty in the first degree," which carried with it the penalty of death either by shooting or hanging. The laws of Nevada inflict the death penalty only in certain cases of murder, this being one of them, and the choice of being shot or hanged remained with the prisoner. Judge Taber gave the prisoner until the morning of October 18th to make his choice when the judge would then pronounce the death sentence.

When the district court opened the morning of October 18, 1917, the court room was filled with jurors, the additional panel of seventy-five reporting at that time . . . The condemned man was brought in and he walked with a steady step to his accustomed seat, which he had occupied for the *past three weeks.*

"I choose to be shot, Your Honor," said Ben Kuhl when Judge Taber asked him if he had made his choice.

The date of execution was fixed by the judge for Thursday, January 10, 1918. Sheriff Harris left with Ben Kuhl that afternoon on the train to deliver the condemned man to the warden of the State Penitentiary.

On his way to the train Kuhl maintained the same stoical indifference that characterized his demeanor throughout the trial and from the time he was arrested. He spoke in a low, even voice to a few acquaintances on the way to the train and from the car window. As the train pulled out on what was to be his final ride, his last words were to his mother who was there to say goodbye.

"Goodbye, Mother."

His mother bore up bravely under the strain, and at no time gave way to her feelings.

"Goodbye, Son," she said. It was evident that she bled internally for her son who must pay the penalty for his crime with his own life. She had the sincere sympathy of the community and all who knew her.

The next case was that of Edward Beck, one of the three charged. Since many similar features, which would come up again, had been fought out and decided by the court, it was assumed that neither of the two remaining cases would take as much time as the Kuhl case.

Beck's long confinement had made him nervous and frightened and he showed the effects when he took the witness stand on October 15, 1917. Beck, born in Finland, spoke broken English which made it difficult for the jurors to hear his answers as he uttered in a toneless and impassive manner. It took about an hour for him to tell his story.

The following morning, October 16th, the verdict of the jury in the Beck case was — "Guilty of murder in the first degree, with life sentence." The prisoner was keyed up to the breaking point and when the clerk read the verdict, Beck was apparently surprised that he had escaped the death penalty, nevertheless the night of the sentencing and the next day he seemed despondent.

Beck was charged with complicity in the murder of Fred Searcy, the Jarbidge stage driver, on the evening of December 5, 1916. That Kuhl had a companion, the State was positive as the footprints of two men were clearly shown but the State had not been able to disclose the companion. There was hope that Beck would take the stand and solve the case of the identity of the second man before this time.

The evidence produced in the first two trials, that of Kuhl and Beck, did not implicate William McGraw sufficiently to put him on trial. According to Beck's story, McGraw knew nothing of the proposed robbery until it was committed, and

108

that he, Beck, had borrowed the gun from McGraw on the plea that Kuhl wanted to go deer hunting. Therefore, upon the dismissal of the murder charge, Billy McGraw was released from the county jail.

In January, 1918, the Ben E. Kuhl case was brought before the Supreme Court on a motion for a new trial to be argued March 2nd at ten in the morning. Attorney H.P. Hale (who took Mr. Caine's place when he said at the end of the Elko District trial that he did not have the time to spend away from his private practice for a new trial) represented the defense and District Attorney Carville and Deputy Cantwell argued the case for the State. A stay of execution was granted Attorney Hale in Carson City as he argued the Kuhl case to have the death sentence commuted to life imprisonment. The date was reset for the shooting of Kuhl to December 20, 1918.

With Nevada Governor Boyle temporarily away from the bench, Acting Governor Sullivan substituted. He and the Board of Pardons visited Kuhl in the death cell at the prison and listened to the latter's story of the crime. During Kuhl's trial he refused at all stages to make a statement, allowing evidence to pile up against him without making any attempt at refutation. Recently, however, with the apparent purpose of securing a commutation of sentence he expressed a willingness to talk and tell his story. Therefore it was for the purpose of listening to his tale and picking therefrom any extenuating circumstances that might guide them in their judgment that the members of the board, with Clerk Mooney, William Kennett, clerk of the Supreme Court; Attorneys E.E. Caine and Harold Hale visited the condemned man and remained with him for several hours.

In his statement Kuhl admitted the killing of Searcy, but claimed self-defense; though he was engaged in an unlawful proceeding it was his life or the stage driver's at the final moment, when he discovered he was being double-crossed. He stated that the robbery was a "frame-up," arranged between him and Searcy and that Fred had admitted having been engaged in a similar faked robbery in Idaho before and had successfully gotten away with it.

Kuhl said that a few days before the killing he was telling Searcy that he needed money to develop some mining claims in the vicinity of Jarbidge and was unable to get it. It was then that the suggestion was made that there was money coming in on the stage and a hold-up could be arranged. So it was planned that on a certain evening a few days following when it would be known to a certainty that a large amount of money, addressed to one of the saloons in Jarbidge which intended to cash pay checks, would pass through the mails, Kuhl could hold-up the stage. Searcy, after making a resistance that would stand investigation, was to give up the sacks. Searcy was then to delay the arrival into town for a short while so that Kuhl could get back, after caching the loot, and be on hand at the post office when the stage finally arrived. This way Kuhl would be able to prove an alibi.

The scheme was thoroughly rehearsed, according to Kuhl's story to the Governor, visiting board and attorneys, even to the scene of operation. Kuhl had no gun, so it was because of this fact that Ed Beck, an illiterate foreigner and rounder, was brought into the robbery. Kuhl went to Beck to borrow a weapon, and when he stated he had none, Kuhl told Beck to get one from McGraw, who was later arrested as an accomplice.

On the night the money was to come, Kuhl went alone to the appointed place and met the stage, the driver being the only occupant. He jumped aboard the box, according to his story, and for a few minutes discussed the "job" with Searcy. The money was there, $200 in a sack in the boot of the stage and the balance, $3200 in currency, in the registered mail sack. Searcy was willing to give up the silver, saying that that would be enough, and reluctant to cut open the sacks and give up the currency. Then a wrangle between the two men occurred and, Kuhl asserted, Searcy went for his gun. Believing then that Searcy was double-crossing him and fearing for his own safety he shot as the stage driver turned his head, therefore hitting him in the back of the neck. Fred collapsed as he was hit and Ben grabbed his body preventing it from falling from the box of the wagon. He then spoke to the stage driver and getting no response, drew the body down into his lap and, grasping the reins, directed the team into the brush along the side of the old road. It was then that Kuhl's clothing became blood soaked, and finding of the coat and shirt and their production in court was evidence against him in the string of circumstantial evidence.

Kuhl, already in possession of the silver, then made a search for the greenbacks and found them, as he stated, under the cushion of the seat. They were not in the sack, as declared by Searcy. The robber also secured the registered mail and took a number of letters and packages, but in his excitement, he said, he failed to remember whether he had to cut open the sack or if it had already been slit. Securing the $3200 in currency and disposing of the silver in one of the abutments of the bridge that crossed the river near the scene, Ben Kuhl told the men that he made his way back to town and joined the posse to look for the stage and the driver. It was not until he helped take the body of Fred Searcy, the man who double-crossed him, from the seat of the wagon that he was absolutely certain the driver was dead. Disclosing that fact, he then endeavored to cover all possible traces that would connect him with the crime, but he failed.

Kuhl was a man of more or less intelligence and probably self-educated. To the board he told his story in a compact, straightforward manner and no cross-questioning changed the details of his recital. He insisted that the robbery was "framed," that Searcy double-crossed him and that when he shot he believed that the stage driver was going to shoot him.

On the evening of December 13, 1918, Acting Governor Sullivan and the Board of Pardons took final action in the case of Kuhl. By a vote of 3 to 2, Governor Sullivan, Attorney General Thatcher and Chief Justice McCarran voting in the affirmative, and justices Sanders and Coleman in the negative, Kuhl's sentence was commuted to life imprisonment. Warden Henrich removed the committed man, who had been under constant guard the past seven weeks, from the death cell to the cell house. Many facts, withheld from the press, and given to the board, subsequently may have had a lot to do in influencing the board in its determination.

With Ben Kuhl's confession at the Nevada State Prison in Carson City before the Governor and the Board of Pardons, one very important fact was substantially proved — that of the palm print theory advanced by the prosecuting attorneys at the

110

time of Kuhl's trial in Elko District Court. That cut a big figure and was a most influencing factor in the case.

---

*Ben Kuhl served thirty-five years in prison and then was released on parole. He had been out nearly five years when he became ill with pneumonia and died.

*This is my own information. I have no definite research to substantiate it.

CHAPTER 23

War had been declared in Europe the midsummer of 1914. When the United States joined the Allies, the small towns and cities sent their quota of young men. Jarbidge suffered a mortal blow. Some of the best young men had been going to the 'front.'

The community with five hundred residents had sent thirty-three of the pick of the young fellows; they were training at some of the camps or already "Somewhere in France." The Jarbidge Red Cross branch had a membership of three hundred adults and a Junior Red Cross of twenty-five members, sending in a total of $840 in cash to the Elko Headquarters.

Hattie, along with the majority of women of Jarbidge, were patriotic and met twice-a-week to knit, work and sew on articles for the sick and wounded or for the boys in the trenches.

Wednesday was ladies night at the Clubhouse and they gave a card party to secure funds for a new and larger flag pole. The ladies wanted to display their Red Cross

Service flag below the Stars and Stripes. The Service flag had sixty stars as most of the patriots were members of the Red Cross and the Commercial Club, therefore it was thought best to make the Service flag a popular town flag.

Because of the boost in property and production, the Elkoro Mill and Mine were experiencing difficulty in finding working men since so many young had gone to war. The company had bought surrounding claims, including the Starlight Mine and small Mill for which they paid Will Martin, my uncle, $140,000. This was a small fortune those days. Uncle Will took $70,000 and his partners, his brother Charlie and Bill Roland shared the remainder.

That winter, influenza which had broken out in Spain, swept through Europe and in no time cases were mounting in New England, Chicago and Kansas City. Only a matter of days and deaths were numerous from the dreaded disease in Colorado, Nevada and all through the West. Cases started showing in Jarbidge and Pavlak. The school was closed and people avoided public gatherings.

Jack volunteered his services and helped care for the sick and those who succumbed to the disease. Mamie Swanson helped nurse the sick. Bill Port assisted Mamie and worked along with the crew of volunteers helping in any way he could. Wooden coffins were made in the town, and gravediggers worked many hours in the cemetery a mile north of the camp. Doctor Wright, the Elkoro Company doctor, worked until he was exhausted trying to save lives of the old men who lived alone in shacks and had no one to care for them.

Papa left home early in the mornings and came home after dark. Mamma had him change his clothes in the woodshed before coming into the house around the family. One night when he came home sick and had a temperature, we were worried. Mamma gave him medicine and put him to bed. She was concerned and sat watching by the bedside for hours. But Papa slept and after a good night's rest he was all right and away again helping the less fortunate. Everybody wore gauze masks on the streets and we had a piece of asafetida sewn in a cotton sack hanging on a ribbon around our necks under the clothing. Smell as it did when we got warm, yet it was supposed to help keep the influenza away.

The four-bed hospital up Bear Creek Street South was always full. We went there to have the 'flu' shots. Mamma saw Dr. Wright give Grace and me the shot, then she started to faint. As soon as she stepped out into the fresh air she felt better and went back for her shot. Papa said that two of the young women from the "Red Light District" came up to help nurse the sick. Jarbidge was one of the lucky mining camps, as we came through the epidemic with few deaths. We always believed it was because so many precautions were taken and sanitation was good.

It was the month of March and the weather had been unpredictable with rain, snow, sleet, wind and occasional sunshine. The Commercial Club had sent eight men

to shovel the snow drifts from the Crippen Grade to make it easier for wagon traffic. The town people hoped that soon autos would be able to travel into the camp.

Mamma liked to play the card game of 500 and was so good that she was one of the few who started with a handicap. Then she usually came home with one of the useful and worthwhile prizes that the ladies offered. She also enjoyed the friendship of the ladies and helped with many functions of the town and club. One of the highlights of her days was the horseback riding club to which she and Pearl belonged.

Spring held some interesting events for the town of Jarbidge. Jimmy Johns and Lillian Smith quietly left town and the next news heard they were married. Since Jimmy had always been one of the leaders of the charivaris heretofore, he had one coming. The ladies turned out to help give the happy couple a rousing, rattling and noisy reception.

Jimmy worked for months in the early days to prove Jarbidge a promising camp and allowed every prospector to come up to the Flaxie Mine and fill his pockets with high grade specimens to be sent all over the country to show there was good gold ore in the Jarbidge mines.

We had thirty-five pupils attending the Jarbidge school. There had never been any need for more than the one log room until the increase and now the county school district had to add another room to the schoolhouse with a cloakroom connecting the two rooms. Also the county employed another teacher. First through fourth grades held classes in the new room and fifth through eighth grades met in the old building. A bell tower was constructed on the front of the school. We were all proud of the addition and pleased when our turn came to ring the bell for school to begin.

One school morning that same March, Grace and Wilma Silvers saw smoke coming from the ceiling around the stovepipe. They called to the teacher and she got all the children out of the older room, but not until the fire had burned down through the beaver-board ceiling. Then it spread so rapidly that the whole interior was a mass of flames by the time the chemical hand-pulled wagon arrived on the scene. The two windows blew out with considerable force just as the chemical arrived and a solid sheet of flames came pouring out of both windows. But within fifteen minutes after the chemical stream was turned into the room the fire was out.

In short time a bucket line was established to the river about sixty feet away, and with two solid lines of both men and women passing the buckets of water soon the charred timbers were completely quenched. The fire was confined wholly to the older room. We all were thankful for the chemical wagon.

The upper grade students were so fortunate to have such a devoted resident, Mr. Nick Vuckovich, who gave them the use of his new cabin until their room could be repaired.

When Papa went to work for the Elkoro Company Warehouse and we left our home in Pavlak and lived in a company house in Jarbidge, we had many adjustments to make.

"I surely miss my chickens and the eggs; there just isn't enough room here for a chickenhouse," complained Mamma. "But we are closer to Jack's work in Jarbidge, and — well, I guess we are better off, at least we have running water and a sink in this house. Girls, I need some eggs and I want you to go below town and get me this basket full from Mrs. Zacharias. You know the place, Gracie. But as you pass those 'houses' down there before you cross the bridge, look straight ahead and don't be gawking at something you should not be. Do you hear me, girls? And do not talk to anyone as you pass through that section."

We knew very well where she meant and were excited over the idea of getting a chance to pass along the road in that 'district.'

"But, Mamma," said Grace, almost pleading. "People say that Alice is beautiful and came from a big city, maybe New York, or somewhere—. That she has a daughter away in school."

"How do you know all that? Have you seen her on the street?"

"One day I saw her in the post office," I said, "and she is pretty. I heard Mr. Fleming call her Alice and she was getting a money order. She had a red velvet dress on and her eyes were dark and eyelashes so long."

Grace interrupted: "George Urdahl tells us about their houses and that those ladies are real nice to him. He delivers groceries after school almost every day and the ladies give him fifty cents. Then the store gives him fifty cents and he takes his little wagon down and brings back the empty whiskey bottles to the saloons and they give him ten cents for every bottle. See how much money he makes?"

"I wonder if his Auntie knows about this," Hattie said as if to barely whisper. "Well, I'll not be the one to carry the story to her. It is none of my business."

"You know, Mamma, he listens to a big Victrola sometimes," I broke in on her thoughts. "Says they let him play any record he wants."

"Well, let me explain something to you girls and I hope you listen carefully. Nice women or young girls never go into saloons or the wrong part of town. Sometimes young women fall in with evil companions and are lonely, or they lose their way in life and they take to drinking. They are soon in the district like that one. I know they send money to us for our Christmas plays and for benefits. I really feel sorry for the young girls who have become unfortunate. It is the older woman they call the 'Madam' who should know better." Mamma was not bitter and explained very well. We tried to understand. She said that there were some ladies, wives of the miners, who were fanatic on the idea of the district being there, but she was not. That some wives were not much better than those girls! And for us to go on and get the eggs, she needed them right away.

Grace and I started out on the run. We knew where the folks lived who had chickens and sold eggs, sometimes they sold milk too, since they had cows.

The Jarbidge "red light district" was comprised of a cluster of five log cabins in the northern end of town. For the first years of the camp the road north and to Idaho crossed the river above the 'district,' but later the bridge was built just below the cabins; therefore the road passed in front of their houses. These brothels were operated with no outward appearance of advertising.

Of the five parlor cabins, one was conducted by Alice and "Midnight George," her pander. The houses looked comfortable, with a main room on the front and bedrooms and kitchen as low-ceilinged extensions, a woodshed and privy in the back.

We passed through the 'district' with eyes wide open, forgetting that we were not to gawk from side to side. We could hear the stem-winded record players going, but saw no one. I mentioned to Grace that I didn't see any red lights hanging by the doors, and look as I did, I could not see any naked ladies in the front rooms.

The ladies' club was to meet at our house the first of June. Mamma had been cleaning house, washing windows, polishing floors and furniture. The weather for the occasion was sunny and beautiful.

116

I was enthusiastic about the party. School had ended for the season and sometimes Muriel and Dorothy came with their mothers and we played with my kittens or sewed on doll clothes.

"I will pick you some wild flowers and fern, Mamma."

"All right, Honey, just a few; I won't have a place for a large bouquet."

When Pappa came home from work, Mamma said, "Jack, I saw an animal run in the woodshed a short while ago. Maybe a rockchuck or raccoon. Will you look for it?"

"Yes, probably a chipmunk, but I'll get Spot, the dog, to help me find it and run it out."

He checked the small woodpile in the shed, under some tools and shovels and no animal. Then he looked inside of a stovepipe which was lying on the dirt floor of the shed.

"Here it is," he said, as he peered into one end of the long pipe. "Now, Spot, you get ready to chase it out of the shed when I turn the pipe up." Jack called to the dog that lay waiting for the chance to catch the animal. We all stood watching, ready for the chase.

When Jack lifted the pipe and the pretty black, bushy tailed animal with the long white stripe down its back emerged, we knew it was too late to stop Spot. Mr. Skunk lifted his tail, sprayed the dog in the face and also the dirt floor of the woodshed and everything around.

Grace and I screamed and ran. So did Mamma. Spot yelped and cried like a pup. Papa cursed. "How the hell did I know that was a skunk? Hattie, couldn't you tell when it came into the shed what it was? Just look at all the trouble that thing has caused."

Hattie had returned to the door of the shed holding a hankie to her nose. "Well, Jack, couldn't you see in the pipe?"

"Hell, no! It was dark in there."

"Oh! My party," cried Hattie. "What will I do tomorrow? It stinks terribly; the smell is coming into the kitchen. I have cleaned and baked for this ladies' card day." Mamma was in tears. Grace and I giggled and Papa laughed. But — really it wasn't funny.

"I will take care of it, Kid. Don't cry or blame me."

Papa removed all wood and tools and saddles from the shed. Then he hauled wheelbarrows of fresh dirt in to cover the putrid ground floor. It did wonders for the sickening odor, but it took many hours of work.

The party went on as scheduled the next day and was a big success, with the kitchen door closed.

"Hattie, you are the best pastry and dessert cook," said Mrs. Baker. And the other ladies agreed. Hattie took the compliment very graciously and thanked them.

CHAPTER 24

On returning to his home in Jarbidge after serving in World War I, a handsome soldier fell desperately in love with Dollie, the most beautiful girl in the red-light district. This romance was known throughout the town, but the well-loved soldier cared not what the people said.

Dollie was a radiant, green-eyed redhead and spoke with a cultured Southern accent. She had an enigmatic smile that set her apart from the other women. Her face gave no evidence of dissipation, her clothes no hint of her profession. She would never reveal her past and how she came to be a lady of ill repute. He thought, how could a youthful, ravishing feminine personality come to that. Nevertheless, he did not let it alter his love for her.

The war had given him a sense of reality, showed him another side of life which had not existed in the secluded family life of his youth.

The soldier's mother and father were immigrants from Sweden and he was their only child. He was born after they arrived in the United States and they had come to Jarbidge in the early days of the camp. How they loved their son and thanked God that he returned safely to them after the war.

This love affair would not last, his folks were sure. Their son, who had resumed his work in the Elkoro Mill, would soon forget this unfortunate girl.

However, he was not to be dissuaded. One moonlight night in late June when the pungent fragrance of the blooming lilac bushes filled the air, they sat on the back steps of the log cabin which was Dollie's home and place of business.

The soldier begged her to marry him.

"I love you too much to marry you, darling," she told him, heartbroken. "You can't marry a brothel girl. It would ruin your life. Your mother and father would never forgive you, nor accept me. No, dear, this town is too small."

"We will leave Jarbidge, and be married and I will find work in Idaho. There are many mills in operation in the West where I can use my skill. We will bury your past and start a new life."

As if to persuade her, he pointed out impetuously, "Mattie Silks married gambler Cort Thomson and Jennie Rogers married Jack Woods."

"But they had nothing to lose," she argued, rather shamefully.

118

Dolly was weeping then and he pulled her against him. He buried his face in her soft hair, as he too was crying. The warmth of her body and the soft scent of her delicate perfume seemed to touch his very soul. He could not lose Dollie; he really loved her.

"Dolly dear . . ."

His fumbling warm lips found hers and she responded eagerly. Knowing this wasn't right, still she pressed closer to him. Dolly was experiencing a true love, but for him . . . perhaps it was infatuation.

She pushed him away and his arms fell. A shaft of light coming from the open door revealed her face and he could see her tear stained green eyes as they sparkled in the moonlight. She looked up into his blue serious eyes.

"No, Darling, I won't marry . . . because I love you so."

Dry-eyed, she watched her heartbroken lover stumble down the road, cross the bridge and turn into his home. Reluctantly, she went back to her room and removed the chatelaine watch pinned to her shirtwaist. She sat with the watch cupped in the palm of her hand, waiting — waiting for the hour of midnight when her lover was to go to work on the graveyard shift at the mill.

The whistle blew and the men were changing shifts . . . he was not there. He had gone to his little cabin where he slept, not far from his folks' home, and there he drank what the miners called a cyanide cocktail, and fell dead across his bed.

CHAPTER 25

It was November, 1919, early in the month, to be exact the third of November, and the weather was whimsical in Jarbidge. Those late fall days might start with sunshine and end with a blizzard of snow which could melt and fill the streets with slush. Children had started thinking of getting out their sleds and women were canning fruits, making gooseberry and chokecherry jelly; garden vegetables were put in tubs of sand-soil in the cellars to be used during the long winter months. The town businesses had set in a large supply of provisions. The atmosphere tingled with a sense of prosperity and the future looked rosy as the mines were producing and mills were running twenty-four hours a day. Population had jumped a couple hundred because Guggenheim's Elkoro had extended their properties and payroll had increased; also, since June, the Elkoro had been producing the State's largest amount of gold.

Gertie McCullough's three-story hotel, a frame structure, kept filled to capacity. Simon's Movie House ran motion pictures three nights a week. The Log Cabin, Crescent and Mint saloons on the west side of the street and Success saloon on the east side were making their bonanzas other than mining.

"I was working night shift at the Starlight," said Jewel Martin. "I'd quit the Long Hike because the boss put me in one of those holes that caved in, with soft walls and I got knocked down twice. Didn't have a fire in the change room. We used to come down home wet, clothes would be about froze on us. So I come down that night wet. I went to bed — but hadn't gotten to sleep when I heard 'Fire! Fire!' Jumped up and put on some clothes, dry ones, mind you, and was helping Gertie take some of her things out of the hotel when in came the men with the fire hose hollerin' 'get out of the way.' Before I could get out of their way, here came the water full force — so I was all wet again. But it didn't dampen my spirits as that was a damn big fire and I tried to help the unfortunate as much as I could."

It was such an early morning hour that men and women were half dressed in the street, trying to save what they could. But the fire which swept along by a high wind down the canyon jumped from one building to another. It started on the west side of the street and crossed, catching buildings on the east side. Just above the lumber building and yard was an old laundry with tubs and equipment in the building, but a family of seven didn't use it as a laundry. They lived there and the father cobbled shoes in the front and made the back section into a rooming house. The fire burned the family out.

The fury and uproar grew to an unorganized pandemonium with people running through the street and calling out:

"How'd it get started?"

"Will it get to my place?"

But no one stopped to listen. The gluttonous tongues of flame began to arch across the street and spaces, dropping sparks and billowing black smoke into the sky. Between the crackling timber sounds came more explosions, bottles bursting and searing noises as the water hit the hot glasses in the saloons.

Word got around: "Now we'll be havin' to use sticks of dynamite, blastin' powder, to stop this damn fire. It might jump the river and take the mill." But the flames kept to the business district and main street, never getting to the mill structures nor the southern end of town. Nevertheless, it was the worst fire Jarbidge ever went through.

The man-drawn fire hose (on a frame connecting two large wheels) was attached to the fire hydrant in the middle of town, but, at this stage, it had little more effect than a garden hose. A hay storage shed burned, but the kids ran and got the cow out. The fire spread from one saloon to another. They said the money in the safes melted and the kids lost no time in going to the smoldering places and gouging out the molten coins which some had become; others were whole but charred black.

The fire fighters saved the Commercial Clubhouse. What a miracle! Where the festive dances took top town billing and the children's Christmas parties, school plays or song-fests had a special meaning for those participating and for their families. The hall was where they held prize fights, after pulling in a movable ring in the building and covering the glistening, waxed maple floor with a specially made, huge canvas. Hallelujah! The clubhouse was saved from the fire.

Jarbidge went back to rebuilding but not as other burned-out mining camps had. The Success saloon owner moved to Elko and other saloon owners and hotels did not rebuild. The fire had burned fifteen buildings, all of them business houses of the town.

Chapter 26

Mamma had definitely decided that their two daughters should have the best education she and Jack could afford and arrange for them—and secondly, that the girls would not go away alone to a boarding school or live with a friend or relative when it came time for them to attend high school. Jack and she would take them. Many talks, even quarrels, had arisen over this matter in the past year as Grace was soon to enter high school. Mamma was not to be dissuaded. What they would live on was for Jack to work out, but even if he wouldn't leave Jarbidge—she would.

Hattie had sisters in California and she could always go there, as she had reminded him. Papa asked Mamma if she wanted her sisters or him.

"That isn't fair, Jack," said Mamma, "you know the Bluster hasn't brought us a good future and now you are working for wages. Why can't you go away and work for wages where there are more conveniences? You are a good meat cutter, get a job as a butcher."

"Now Hattie, I know how you tried to make the best of Jarbidge," he reminded her, "it was really not your life, but you did it for me and the children. It takes a lot of love to stick with a man who mines for a living . . . "

"Just talk," Hattie interrupted. "Talk and excuses, you know I've enjoyed my life here—my friends and my wonderful horse, and all." She hesitated . . . "but there comes a time . . . " Her voice trailed off as she walked away.

One day, when Mamma, Gracie and I were visiting Aunt Pearl in Twin Falls, we went to the circus. My legs began hurting and soon the pain was excruciating. I told Mamma and she immediately wanted to go back to Auntie's home.

"Just let me look one more time at the elephants and giraffes, Mamma, please?" How I wanted to stay and watch those huge animals and all the other events the circus had to offer, but the pain was too great.

A terrible fever and leg ailment struck me and crippled my skinny limbs. Doctors said it was lack of lime in the water or too much snow water and the bones hadn't hardened. We stayed in Twin Falls and I was bedfast for a week. As soon as I was up a little we returned to Jarbidge. I couldn't go to school because I fell when I tried to walk; soon I was using two canes and scraping along the floor at home. Still the pain was there in my legs. Little was known then about rheumatic fever.

123

About a month later, while Mamma's pent-up fears and resentments had been building, I knew what lay in store for Papa when he came home. Grace was out riding her horse and I was propped-up on the front room couch.

"We are leaving for Southern California, Jack." Papa had barely taken off his hat when Mamma's words flew at him like arrows. "And don't get one of your brain storms, either. The most important thing in the world now is to get my little Helen well." She looked straight at him with fire in her eyes. Those large, round, hazel eyes that were so beautiful ten years ago and now were tired and showed a troubled, defeated look. "What a pity to see Helen fall and not be able to help herself up. It breaks my heart." Mamma looked at me for a moment as though I had no business listening.

"I will see the boss tomorrow," said Papa, "have him get someone to take my place at the warehouse and we can leave in a week."

Mamma had won, even though Papa was reluctant to leave Jarbidge, the familiar mountains and people. He knew my health depended on getting out of the cold and snow, or, at least it seemed that was the right thing to do.

Our house was soon in a turmoil of activity, getting ready to go where the sun shone every day. We packed what we could get into our 1914 Buick touring car. So many things we were leaving behind, the organ, Mamma's guitar, my cats and kittens; but most of all our Pavlak home which held so many beautiful memories.

The trip to Southern California was long, dusty and tiresome for all of us. My legs hurt most of the time. I had to be lifted into and out of the car. Papa decided on a shorter way so we followed a rutty road which crossed alkali flats and bounced down the little-traveled routes. I remember we stopped for the night on a wind-swept, barren place, so unlike the Jarbidge surroundings. To build a fire, Grace had to pick up pieces of sagebrush and dried cowchips, and Mamma cooked dinner (Papa helping her, as always). They made a bed for me on the back seat of the Buick while they bedded down beside the car with blankets and tarps which had been packed in and on the running boards of the vehicle.

When we arrived in San Diego, we rented a small house located next to that of one of Mamma's sisters. Of course it could not last, our little family was to be separated again. Papa said to Mamma, "Now, Hattie, we can't live on fruits and flowers in California, I've searched for work—this city life is not for me . . . " Papa's intentions had been good but when he heard about a small copper mine and prospect in Arizona, there is where he went.

My health grew better and I entered school. Frightened by all the kids in such a large school I didn't make friends but stayed by myself. I drew unwanted attention by the odd manner in which I used my legs, the knees didn't bend properly so I slipped my legs out to the side and around forward. Of course this made me a sensitive and unhappy child and at an age of ten years.

When the summer came and we followed Papa to the dry and hot weather of Arizona, I regained the correct and complete use of my legs.

Papa was copper mining and there was hope and faith in his eyes. Maybe what he wanted wasn't the metal, but the enticing hunt and everlasting love of the elusive game.

124

Arizona and the copper mine only lasted one and a half years. Papa was restless and wanted to pull out for Jarbidge and resume work on the Bluster hill. It was sad that our family should be separated again, but Papa still had visions of great possibilities in the Jarbidge District. The Elkoro was still running and doing quite well. Dear Mamma, who was so dedicated, said she'd take her girls back to California for school.

Years passed. When we could afford the train fare, Mamma, Grace and I visited Papa during summer vacations.

After I met Roy Wilson in San Diego and we were married, I took him to meet Papa and see the town of my childhood. He was caught by the magnetism of that forest canyon and the pine-scented, fresh air. His curiosity about the history of the district mounted as he peered at the deteriorating, weathered mills, crumbling mines and caved-in tunnels, some portals closed with sliding rocks and debris.

He enjoyed mining and packing horses with sacks of ore, the ore which Papa found on the surface of the Bluster hill. Jack and Bud got along well. It was far removed from the oceans and ships of my husband's years of living, but he loved Jarbidge and all it had to offer. Everytime he could get leave of absence from the Navy, we went to Jarbidge.

Mrs. Baty owned and operated a grocery store. She even served ice cream sodas at her forty-year-old fountain and counter; or we sat on white wrought iron chairs at a small, round table and ate banana splits.

Rachel Baty was also the district recorder and typed on an antique typewriter.

John Berry opened his store everyday; the store of never-ending notions, shoes, levis, hardware and cosmetics. George Urdahl had the gasoline service station and garage. John (the basque) Ensunsa operated a lively saloon and cooled his draft beer from the snowdrifts at the Bear Creek Summit for as many months as there was snow.

One year, "Old Dick" Papa's faithful horse, died and my father said he would be next to go. The next spring the dear body which had climbed so many mountains and done the hardest work, slipped away. Papa had passed on without realizing a real gold strike. I always knew, although his body gave out and health was bad, he passed away with a broken heart.

Bud and I continued to visit Jarbidge and soon bought a nice cabin. For the steep and rough trips, we towed a military four-wheel jeep to be kept at the cabin; in fact, it was the first such vehicle brought into and used in the district.

Charlie Hawkinson, one of the 1912 prospectors who walked into the booming camp and had remembered me when I was a tow-headed child, went with us on one of our delightful but scary jeep trips. His first words, upon alighting, were, "What pow'r, never saw such pow'r."

I sat beside my husband one sunny July morning, as he drove "Suzie, the jeep" along the canyon road from Jarbidge to Pavlak. I reminisced and recalled the time when this was the site of a mining community, important to Nevada's history. I feared Pavlak's tale would be lost forever unless I could tell what I knew of its significant early days. The existence of the small community was brief, but residents built log cabins as my folks did. We lived in our home for nine years.

"Can I find where my childhood home was? The willows have grown thick and tall, the river has changed its channel and the banks are so steep," I said to Bud. "It seems even the landscape has changed. But somewhere here was the house I knew as a child."

Bud saw my emotion and said regretfully. "Your house was torn down, so I heard, together with the barn and other buildings, and carted off to be sold for lumber."

I gazed at the only remaining building, caved-in and decaying, and precariously leaning before the threat of another winter. Then I recognized the Pavlak Post Office where Mamma was postmaster.

For a moment I was speechless. Resentment tore at my heart. Why did Papa sell our home and let them tear it down? It was here, I thought, we had made a good life and in my heart I cherished that bit of land. Could I find where the foot bridge

126

crossed the river, where Mamma's flower garden was and Papa's vegetable and potato patch? Even the hop vines had been torn away from the place where the porch was, just a few short steps from the river's edge.

My mind engrossed, I was lost in thought for a short while. The sound of my husband's voice brought me to my senses.

"Sweetheart, do not be sad, time does go by." I tried to shake off the depression which I had lapsed into.

"Yes! I know there are many changes through the years. One is that the forest service has added camping spaces in this area. It looks as though the very location of our cabin has since been used by innumerable campers. I hear that one group of deer hunters came last fall and pitched a large cooking and sleeping tent in this area. Now I believe it was on this very spot. They had a modern gas operated power plant among other conveniences. They also flew an American flag and called the site "Little America" not knowing the history of the Pavlak district ... That is progress."

"Come on, Towhead, (Bud's pet name for me) let's go on to the Bluster Mine and look over the old tunnel. We can do the assessment work on the two Bluster claims that legally belonged to your father or his heirs."

So we drove a half-mile to the foot of the grade leading to the mine, put the jeep into four-wheel drive and slowly traveled the rough and steep climb. In less than one quarter of a mile we came to the old assay office which was resting on very loose dirt on the upper side of the mountain just above the road.

"Wonder how long that old building will stay there and not fall into the road to block our way?" I asked Bud.

"It may stay for years," he commented, "one never knows. Let's look inside." Some whole, but many broken crucibles cluttered the floor and tables, also bottles of acid and in one corner was a small forge. Correspondence and sheets of assay figures were strewn about.

Just a couple hundred feet from the assay office we came to the ten-stamp mill and the place where the overhead tram buckets came down from the mine head-house and entered the upper part of the mill, where ore in the buckets was dumped into the chute.

The corrugated iron had been taken or had blown from the roof of the old mill. The timbers were weathered by many dry summers and snow-laden winters since my childhood. A chipmunk capered over the splintered boards and off into the sagebrush which now grew along the sides. The quiet shimmering atmosphere was not disturbed by a bell of the tram buckets or the rocks falling into the ore chute. How still the world seemed.

"Let's go!" we said in unison and hopped into the open jeep and began the two mile pull. The zig-zag road, built in 1934, replaced the foot or horse trail that followed closely below the overhead tram, and went through scrub mahogany trees into the pines. It criss-crossed the Pick and Shovel Mine and then climbed to the tunnel of the Success Mine before coming onto the Bluster claims.

We arrived at the north end of the long bunkhouse-and-kitchen that had been built for the miners, sufficient to house thirty-five men. It was empty, even of windows and doors. I gasped when I saw that the large wood and coal stove had been hauled away. I remembered the stove with its two large ovens, in which I baked berry pies. That summer of 1929, I stayed with Papa for five weeks and cooked for him and his two-man crew. Suede Bob and Scottie were working with him at the mine and Bob McVicker and Shorty Roberts were at the mill. Because the tram was in operation I used to send food to the men at the mill, and one day I had baked two berry pies and was going to send the second pie to them.

I recalled that Papa said, "Don't make pets of those chipmunks, Kid. Don't name them. They will make themselves at home on the table and you will be sorry," he continued with a hint of laughter in his voice while trying to appear serious.

But it was lonely through the days and so I enjoyed the presence of the pretty chipmunks running in and out of the open kitchen door, even saying a few words to them while tossing them pecans. They would watch me as they took the nut and sat on their hind legs, with the two front feet quick and nimble as they turned the morsel over and over, nibbling so fast. But it was quite a different story the day I took the pie over to the tram for the mill men. When I returned to the bunkhouse kitchen I found the crust edges of the pie we were to have for dinner had been eaten away.

That evening I said, "Papa, I dislike asking you to do this, but will you please set traps for our friends, the chipmunks?" He answered with a smile and a nod.

We continued on our journey to the mine terminal and how excited I was.

"Bud darling, the old tunnel is still open. It looks dangerous, the timbers are so damp and have rotted away in places, but let's take a chance and go in a short ways."

"I'm game." chuckled Bud, and we got our flashlights and a couple of small sacks to use for ore samples. We kept close together as we entered the cool, murky tunnel. The air got colder and the water was oozing from the side walls as we slipped cautiously along over the rust-corroded tracks. Suddenly as if I heard a voice of admonition, "Darling, should we go back?"

"Whatever you say, Sweetheart, but I think it is all right."

Our curiosity was overwhelming, so we went on into the darkness, holding hands. We moved on slowly until we came to a steel door.

"I never saw this door before, guess it was built when United Eastern Company worked the mine. Was the ore that rich?"

"I've heard said, Towhead, that doors are installed because of the richness of the mine, but this one's purpose may have been to cut off the draft coming from the cross-cut in the tunnel."

"Shall we open it, Bud?"

"As it isn't locked, we will try."

The door squeaked as it yielded to our hard pull. A gust of colder air hit us and the dampness was extreme. But we moved on in a quiet, furtive manner, each grasping the other's arm, wondering — Should we or shouldn't we?

"There hasn't been anyone in this mine for years," I whispered. "The timbers must be dangerously loose and old. The odor of wet ground and rotten logs is strong, but let's try to reach that first station where this tunnel enlarges and three

128

tunnels branch off." We stopped to rest a bit while I continued to tell about the year I helped Papa at the mine.

"One crosscut branched off to the right. One drift followed the vein straight ahead and the other went to the left and finally ended at the terminal of the Success Mine, right out onto the ore dump. You remember we came across that, don't you?"

Before he could answer, I continued: "The ore was very rich where Papa was digging that year, but it was so dangerous that he would not let me get near the *stope*. The ground was sluffing all the time and could not be timbered. He would fill the ore car with the *pay-dirt* and I pushed it out to the entrance. As the tunnel slanted slightly down-grade, I could get the car started and jump on the back ledge and ride it out. Then tip it over to one side to dump the ore into the chute which led to the airway tram and the mill. I then went back with the empty car for another load, sometimes running off the track at the cross-cut corner. Papa would hear me calling and come to put the car back onto the tracks. But . . . . that was years ago and I was a teenager. Youth has so little fear."

We continued our trek and suddenly came onto the station we had wanted to find. After a brief inspection of the area and a small sample of the dirt that had fallen down from the hanging-wall, and a few small rocks to put in the ore sacks, we proceeded to make our way back out of the tunnel. Cautiously we hurried along . . . . by the steel door . . . . . over the old rusty tracks . . . . and to the most welcome daylight of the outside world.

I tried to understand and appreciate the magnitude of that early day gold and silver fever and not berate those who came to "hit it rich" or just had the desire to earn a good living for the family; yet some didn't really accomplish either.

Jarbidge is a place which many people have not yet discovered. One may say it is one of the last Western "outposts."

Somehow . . . . in the summertime, people in cars and pickups and campers drive the twisting, narrow road along the river's edge from Idaho to Jarbidge; or slither down the steep grade from Charleston, to sight-see and enjoy the canyon spectacle, or the soul-restoring scent of pine trees and the romantic tranquility of the quiet.